فرزندان لیر

یک افسانهٔ سلت

The Children of Lir

A Celtic Legend

نژاد سلت حدود ۷۰۰سال قبل از میلاد مسیح در انگلستان زندگی می‌کردند.
سلت‌ها تا ۳۰۰ سال قبل از میلادمسیح از ایرلند تا ترکیه را زیر سلطه داشتند.
عشق وافر به داستان سرایی و قصه گویی وابستگان نژاد سلت در جزایر بریتانیا
شهرت بسزایی دارد.
داستانهای شاه لیر و خانوادهٔ او که خدایان دریا محسوب می شدند، هزاران
سال دهان به دهان گشته است.
لیر در تراژدی شکسپیر لیبر شناخته می شود، و محل اصلی ستایش او لستر
نامیده می شود: لِستر (لیرستر).
فرزندان لیر یکی از آسه قصیدهٔ غم انگیز آ است، در میان همهٔ افسانه های سلت ها،
افسانه ای، به این غم انگیزی و لطافت نیست.

Celts lived in Britain from around 700 BC. By 300 BC the Celts' lands extended from Ireland to Turkey.

The Celtic peoples of the British Isles were well-known for their love of story-telling, stories of Lir and his Family, Gods of the Sea, have been told around the fire for thousands of years. Lir's Welsh equivalent, Llyr, became King Lear in Shakespeare's tragedy, and the principal place of his worship was named after him: Leicester (Llyr-cester).

The Children of Lir is one of the "*Three Sorrows of Storytelling*", in all of Celtic Legend there is no more tender or tragic tale.

English Pronunciation Guide:

Tuatha Dé Danaan	*Too-ha Day Dan-aan*	*Aoife*	*Ee-fa*
Fionnuala	*Fin-oo-la*	*Bodb the Red*	*Bov the Red*
Fiacra	*Fee-ak-ra*	*Sidhe*	*Shee*
Aed	*Ay (rhymes with day)*		

First published 2003 by Mantra
5 Alexandra Grove, London N12 8NU
www.mantralingua.com

British Library Cataloguing in Publication Data:
a catalogue record for this book is available from the British Library.

فرزندان لیر

The Children of Lir

Retold by Dawn Casey

Illustrated by Diana Mayo

Farsi translation by Parisima Ahmadi-Ziabari

mantra

گوش کن! من داستان فرزندان لیر را برایت نقل می کنم.

در زمانهای قدیم و در آغاز آفرینش که فضای سحر آمیزی احساس می‌شد، پادشاهی بنام لیر زندگی می‌کرد.

لیر از نژادی الهی بنام تو-هادی دَن آن بود، که بر همهٔ سرزمین ایرلند فرمانروایی می‌کرد، و همسر او دختر بزرگ شاه شاهان بود. خوشبختی آنها باچهار فرزند تکمیل شده بود: سه پسر و یک دختر، فین اُلا. فین اُلا فرزند اوّل بود و بعداز او ای و بعد دو قلوهای جوان فی اَکرا و کُن بودند. پادشاه عاشق فرزندانش بود وآنها را بیشتر از هر چیز در دنیا دوست میداشت، برای‌مدّتی آنها باشادمانی زندگی می کردند.

Listen! I will tell you the story of the Children of Lir.

Long ago, when the earth was young and there was always magic in the air, there lived a king named Lir.

Lir was one of the Tuatha Dé Danaan, the divine race which ruled over all green Ireland, and his wife was the eldest daughter of the High King.

They were blessed with four children: three sons and a single daughter, Fionnuala. Fionnuala was the eldest and next came Aed, and then the young twins Fiacra and Conn. The king loved his children more than anything else in the world, and, for a while, they were happy.

امّا زود بعد از اینکه دوقلوها متولد شدند، ملکه مُرد. پادشاه قلبش شکست، امّا بچّها به مادر احتیاج داشتند. بنابراین لیر دوباره با دختر دوّم شاه شاهان که ایفا نام داشت ازدواج کرد. ایفا در ابتدا خیلی مهربان بود و همیشه با نشاط و شاد بود. امّا وقتی دید که لیر عمیقاً شیفتهٔ فرزندانش می باشد، کم کم حسادت وجودش را پر کرد. قلب کوچک او پر از نفرت شد و به جادوی سحرآمیز سیاهی روی آورد...

But soon after the twins were born the queen died. The king was heartbroken, but the children needed a mother. And so Lir married again, to the High King's second daughter, Aoife. At first Aoife was caring, and always full of life and laughter. But she saw how deeply Lir loved his children, and she grew jealous. Her light heart grew heavy with hate, and she began to practise dark magic…

یک روز صبح زود ملکه بچها را از خواب بیدار کرد، و در حالیکه خمیازه
می‌کشیدند، آنها را روانهٔ یک دریاچهٔ دورافتاده کرد، که آب تنی کنند.
”عزیزانم شنا کنید، بازی کنید“ او به آنها می‌گفت. صدای او به شیرینی
وغلیظی عسل بود.

Early one morning the queen woke the children and led them, sleepy
and yawning, to a lonely lake, and sent them into the water to bathe.
"Swim and play, my dears," she told them, her voice as sweet and thick
as honey.

سه تا پسر ها در آب پریدند ، داد و فریاد میکردند، امّا فین اُلا شک کرد.
"شنا کنید!" ملکه دستور میداد. فین اُلا خیلی آرام به داخل آب رفت.

The three boys splashed into the water at once, shrieking and shouting,
but Fionnuala hesitated.

"Swim!" the queen commanded. And slowly the girl waded into the water.

فین اُلا زن پدرش را خوب زیر نظر داشت. امّاخشکش زد وقتی که دید ایفا یک عصای جادویی در لابلای چین‌های لباسش دارد.

ملکه دستهایش را بلندکرد و شروع به زمزمهٔ یک ورد مَسخ کننده کرد و عصا را پایین آورد و با آن به نوبت به بالای ابروی‌هر یک از آنها زد.

بلافاصله جایی که فین اُلا، فی اکرا، ای و کُن شنا میکردند، حالاچهار تا قوی سفید زیبا بود.

Fionnuala watched her stepmother. The warmth drained from her body as she saw Aoife draw a Druid's wand from the folds of her cloak.

Raising her arms, the queen began to chant a hypnotic incantation, and she brought the wand down, touching the children, each in turn, upon the brow.

In an instant, where once Fionnuala, Fiacra, Aed and Conn had swum, there now floated four beautiful white swans.

"فرزندان لیر!" ایفا آواز سر داد، "من شما را لعنت کردم! شما ۹۰۰ سال به صورت قو زندگی می کنید! شما باید ۳۰۰ سال در این دریاچه باشید، ۳۰۰ سال در آبهای سرد ایرلند و آخرین ۳۰۰ سال روی اقیانوس اطلس عمیق بگذرانید."

بچها وحشت کرده بودند و بالهایشان را دیوانه وار بهم می زدند، و به او التماس می کردند آنها را آزاد کند. امّا جادوگر می خندید." شما هرگز آزاد نمی شوید تا وقتی که یک ملکه از جنوب با یک پادشاه از شمال ازدواج کند و شما صدای زنگی که نمایانگر پیمان تازه ایی باشد بشنوید."

"Children of Lir!" Aoife intoned, "I curse you! You will live as swans for nine hundred years! You must spend three hundred years here on this lake, three hundred on the cold Irish Sea and the last three hundred on the wild Atlantic Ocean."

The children were terrified and beat their wings frantically, begging her to set them free. But the Sorceress only laughed. "You will never be free, until a queen from the South marries a king from the North, and you hear the sound of a bell ringing out a new faith."

”ای ایفا“ فین اُلا به زن پدرش التماس کرد، ”اینقدر بی رحمی نکن!“
ایفامکثی کرد، و بیاد آورد زمانی که برای بچها مادر بوده است،
و قلب سنگ او کمی نرم شد.
”شما می توانید با صدای خودتان آواز بخوانید و آواز شما شیرین ترین
صدا در تمام دنیا خواهد بود.“
به این ترتیب ملکه از ساحل دور شد.

"Oh Aoife," Fionnuala pleaded with her stepmother, "do not be so cruel!"

Aoife paused, remembering how she had once been a mother to the children, and her hard heart softened a little. "You will be able to sing with your own voices, and your song will be the sweetest that the world has ever heard."

And with that the queen fled from the shore.

او یکسر به سراغ پدرش بو دِ رد پادشاه مقتدر توها- دی‌دَن‌اَن رفت.
امّاشاه بزرگ از کردهٔ دخترش وحشت زده شد. ''ایفا دخترم''، او غرّید،
'' تو چکار ی کردی'' و او با عصای سحرآمیز دخترش را نوازش کرد.
ملکهٔ خیانت کار به یک دیو هوایی تبدیل شد و برای همیشه به
بادها پیوست.
در شبهای طوفانی شما هم می توانید زوزهٔ او را بشنوید.

She ran straight to her father, Bodb the Red, mighty king of
the Tuatha Dé Danaan. But the High King was horrified by his
daughter's deed. "Aoife, my daughter," he boomed, "what
have you done!" and he struck her with his Druid's wand.
The treacherous queen was transformed into a Demon
of the Air, to be tossed on the winds forever.

On a stormy night you can still hear her howls.

در این ضمن شاه لیر همه جا را برای دیدن فرزندانش جستجو می‌کرد.
همینطور که‌به طرف دریاچه آمد فرزندانش که- قو شده بودنداو را صدا
کردند. لیر صدای بچها را شنید،امّا فقط چهار تا قوی سفید دید. بعد،
در یک لحظهٔ وحشتناک او فهمید. پادشاه احساس کرد که،اشک از
چشمانش سرازیر شده است و روی گونه اش‌می غلتد و با عجله‌به‌سوی
فرزندانش رفت، که آنها را در آغوش‌بگیرد، امّا، آنها بدون دستهایشان
نمی توانستد پادشاه را بغل کنند.

Meanwhile, King Lir searched everywhere for his children. As he came
to the lake the swan-children called out his name. Lir heard his children's
voices, but saw only four white swans. Then, in a terrible moment, he
understood. The king felt tears come to his eyes and they rolled down his
cheeks as he rushed to embrace his children, but, without arms, they could
not hug him back.

فین اُلا غصّه را در چهرهٔ پدرش خواند، و با اشتیاق می خواست او را تسلی بدهد، او شروع به آواز خواندن کرد. برادرانش به او پیوستند و آواز بلندی سر دادند. بَه بَه! آن آواز ماه نقره ایی بود. لطیف تر از هر صدایی بود، و شیرین تر از آواز هر پرنده ایی بود. پادشاه در حالیکه به آن موزیک دل انگیز گوش می داد قلب شکسته اش آرام گرفت.

Fionnuala saw the anguish on her father's face, and longing to comfort him, she began to sing. Her brothers joined in, lifting their voices to the skies.

Oh! The silver of the moon was in that song. It was softer than any human voice, and sweeter than any bird song.

As the old king listened to the beautiful music his broken heart was soothed.

پادشاه هر روز به کنار دریاچه می آمد و به آنها گوش می داد.
همهٔ افرادتوها-دی‌دَن اَن و همهٔ ایرلندی ها به کنار دریاچه رفتند تا
آواز ماه نقره ایی قوها را بشنوند.
آواز فوق العادهٔ فرزندان لیر برای ۳۰۰ سال ایرلندی ها را شیفته کرد.
امّا خیلی زود روزی رسید که بچّها - قوها می بایست پدر، سرزمین و
مردم او را ترک کنند، و به دریای خشمگین ایرلند بروند.
تا دورهٔ دوّم تبعید را تکمیل کنند.
قوها به شمال پرواز کردند. آنها هرگز روی پدرشان را دوباره ندیدند.

Day after day Lir came back to the lake to listen.

All the Tuatha Dé Danaan and all the men of Ireland went to the lake
to hear the swans' silver song.

The wondrous singing of the Children of Lir held the people of
Ireland entranced for three hundred years.

But, too soon, the day came for the swan-children to leave their
father and their people, and to go to the angry Irish Sea, to fulfil the
second period of their exile.

The swans flew north. They never saw their father's face again.

دریای ایرلند یک باریکهٔ آب توفانی بین ایرلند و اسکاتلند است.
یک دریای دور افتاده، سرد و ترسناک. آنجا کسی نبود که
آواز آنها را بشنود.آنجا، پرهایشان با بادخیلی سرد یخ زد،
و با شلاق آبهای یخ به صخرهای بی رحم می خوردند.

The Irish Sea is a stormy stretch of water between Ireland and
Scotland. A fierce and freezing sea it was, and lonely. There was no one
to listen to their song.

There, arctic winds froze their feathers, and they were lashed by icy
water, dashed against cruel rocks.

یک شب توفان وحشتناکی وزید.

باد زوزه می کشید و می غرّید، ابرها می‌غریدند. برق آسمان را گویی از هم جدا می‌کرد.قو ها خودشان را به هم جمع کرده بودند و باد سهمناک و امواج دریا آنهارا به این طرف و آن طرف پرت می کرد.

One night a terrible storm rolled in.

The wind howled and moaned, and thunderclouds groaned. Lightning tore the sky. The swan-children were buffeted and flung apart by the wild winds and waves.

فقط یک صخرهٔ دورافتاده که بزرگتر از سر یک خوک آبی نبود در روی آبهای موّاج بلند بود. فین اُ لا با زحمت خودش را به آن رساند و برادرانش را صدا کرد، آنها با احتیاط بالا خزیدند.

ضربه های امواج بر روی صخره ها می شکستند و سرمای سوزندهٔ آنها صخره ها را می شست. قوها به هم چسپیده بودند تا دستخوش امواج‌نشوند. بنابراین خواهر، برادرانش را زیر بالهای خودش جمع کرد و آنها را محکم گرفت. کُن، زیر بال راستش، فی اکرا زیر بال چپ او و ای هم سرش را روی سینهٔ او گذاشت.

Only one solitary rock, no bigger than a seal's head, rose above the crashing water. Fionnuala struggled to that rock, and sang out to her brothers until they crawled up to safety.

The pounding waves exploded against the rock drenching them with water, piercing cold, and they had to cling together to save from being washed away.

But the sister gathered her brothers under her wings and held them close, Conn under her right wing and Fiacra under her left, and the last brother, Aed, laid his head against her breast.

۳۰۰ سال به آرامی در آن محل متروک گذشت، امّا بالاخره وقت آن رسید که قسمت‌سوّم و آخر طلسم کامل شود.

"ما باید به اقیانوس‌اطلس برویم" فین اُلا به برادرانش گفت. "امّا بر سر راهمان بر روی وطن خودمان پرواز می کنیم تا پدرمان را ببینیم."

قوها شبانه پرواز کردند. بالهای سفید آنها با هم می زد و در نور مهتاب می درخشید.

Three hundred years passed slowly in that desolate place, but at last it was time to fulfil the third and final stage of their long enchantment.

"We must go to the Atlantic," Fionnuala said to her brothers. "But on the way, let us fly over our home and see our father."

The swans flew through the night, their wide white wings beating as one, and shining in the moonlight.

در پگاه بر روی سرزمین دوران کودکی خود پرواز می کردند، و با دقت به زمین نگاه می کردند، و امیدوار بودند که یک نظر اجمالی به قلعهٔ پدرشان بیندازند. امّا جایی که زمانی قصر با شکوه لیر بر پا بود، چیزی جز گزنه‌ها دیده نمی شد، که با وزش باد تکان می خوردند. پدرشان سالیان درازی بود که مرده بود.

قوها آواز غمگینی را سر دادند، به پرواز ادامه دادند.

In the pale morning they flew over the land of their childhood, and scanned the ground, hoping to catch a glimpse of their father's fort. But where Lir's splendid palace had once stood, there was now nothing but nettles, blowing in the breeze. Their father was long since dead.

Keening a lament, the swans flew on.

بالاخره آنها به ساحل اقیانوس اطلس رسیدند، و در آنجا، آنها یک
جزیرهٔ کوچک بنام آینیش گلورا پیدا کردند. آنجا، بعداز مدتها
مستقر شدند. بار دیگر آنها بوسهٔ لطیف آفتاب را احساس
کردند که استخوانهایشان را گرم می‌کرد.

At last they came to the shores of the Atlantic Ocean, and there, they
found a tiny island, named Inish Glora. Here, at long last, they rested.
Once more they felt the gentle kiss of the sun, warming their bones.

قوها در آنجا به انتظار نشستند، و آواز خواندند. آنها آوازهای
قدیمی را که از دوران جوانی بخاطر داشتند می خواندند، و همهٔ
پرندگان زمینی و دریایی در آن جزیره جمع شده بودند تا آواز
طلسم شده‌ها را بشنوند.

The swans stayed, waiting, and singing. They sang the Old Songs they
knew from their youth, and all the birds of the land and of the sea flocked
to the island to listen, spellbound.

در آنجا بود که آنها دهقان جوانی را بنام اِوریک ملاقات کردند،
او داستان آنها راشنید، و آن را تعریف کرد.
و در نتیجه داستان زنده نگه داشته شد، و امروزه هم ما آن را نقل
می کنیم. آنها برای مدّتها کس دیگری را ندیدند، تا وقتی که،
یک روز، زاهدی به جزیره آمد.
زاهد مرد مقدسی بود، امّا از نژاد دَن آن نبود، تقریباً ۹۰۰ سال
از زمان کودکی فین اُلا و برادرنش می‌گذشت و همه چیز تغیر
کرده بود. نژ ادجدیدی بر سرزمینهای سبز و ایرلند
حکومت می‌کردند.خدایان قدیمی زیر زمین رفته بودند،
و به شی و حورّیان افسانه ایی تغیر کرده بودند.

It was here that they met the young farmer named Evric, who heard their story, and who told it. And so their tale was kept alive, and we tell it still today.

They saw no one else for a long time, until, one day, a hermit came to the island.

The hermit was a holy man, but he was not of the Danaan, for it was almost nine hundred years since Fionnuala and her brothers were children, and things had changed.

A new race now ruled the green lands of Ireland. The old gods had gone underground, transformed into *Sidhe*, Faery Folk, and faded into myth.

زاهد داستان و افسانهٔ فرزندان لیر را شنیده بود. وقتی نوای طلسم شدهٔ آنها راشنید به نزدیک آنها آمد. ''نترسید،'' او گفت. ''من به شما کمک خواهم کرد.''

The hermit had heard tell of the legend of the Children of Lir. When he heard their enchanting music he approached them. "Do not be afraid," he said. "I will help you."

زاهد در آینیش گلورا معبدی ساخت، و فرزندان لیر صدای بلند و رسای یک زنگ را در جزیره شنیدند، صدای زنگ در همهٔ جزیره پیچیده بود. در همان وقت، در جایی دور تر مقدمات یک عروسی فراهم می‌شد، برای یک پادشاه از شمال و یک ملکه از جنوب. این ملکه هم افسانهٔ قوها را شنیده بود، و آنها را برای خودش می خواست. او از همسر جدیدش خواست آنها را برای او بیاورد و به عنوان هدیهٔ عروسی به اوبدهد، بنابراین همسرش برای گرفتن قوها عازم شد.

The hermit built a chapel on Inish Glora, and the Children of Lir heard the loud clear sound of a bell ringing, pealing out across the island.

At the same time, far away, wedding preparations were being made, for a king from the North was to marry a queen from the South.

This queen had also heard tales of the fabulous swans, and she wanted them for herself. She asked her new husband to get them for her, as a wedding gift, and so he set out to capture them.

البته زاهد مانع او شد، امّا پادشاه با سختی قوها را بسیج کرد، با زحمت آنها را گرفت، که با خودش آنها را ببرد.

Of course the hermit refused him, but the king seized the swans roughly, meaning to drag them away.

The moment the king touched the swans the spell was broken. The swans' plumage fell away, revealing, not the radiant forms of Danaan youths, but four shrivelled and wasted bodies, over nine hundred years old - three aged men and one ancient woman. As the feathers floated to the ground the last breath of life left their bodies.

در همان لحظه‌ ایی که پادشاه قوها را گرفت طلسم شکسته شد.
پر و بال قوها ریخت، آنچه باقی ماند، نشانی از جوانان نژاد
دَن اَن نبود، امّا چهار بدن که در مدت ۹۰۰ سال تحلیل
رفته بودند و چروکیده شده بودند.
سه مرد مسّن و یک زن پیر. همانطور که پرهایشان روی زمین
می ریخت آخرین‌نفس زندگیشان را می کشیدند.

”ما ها را کنار هم در یک گور دفن کنید“ فین‌اُلا تقاضا کرد.
بنابراین همینطور هم شد. فین اُلا آرمیده بود و برادرانش را با
خودش گرفته بود، کُن در سمت راست او، فی اکرا در سمت
چپ او، و بالاخره ای روی سینهٔ او بود.
عاقبت فرزندان لیر به آرامش رسیدند. امّا زاهد تا آخرین روزهای
زندگیش برای آنها غصّه دار بود.

"Bury us together, in one grave," Fionnuala asked.
And so it was done. Fionnuala lay holding her brothers close, with
Conn on her right, and Fiacra on her left, and the last brother, Aed, laid
his head against her breast.

And so the Children of Lir found peace at last. But the hermit, it is
said, sorrowed for them to the end of his days.

SIMPLE CHIC *Crochet*

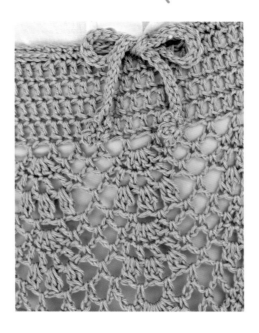

35 STYLISH PATTERNS TO CROCHET IN NO TIME

Susan Ritchie and Karen Miller
of Mrs Moon

CICO BOOKS

LONDON NEW YORK

Published in 2017 by CICO Books
An imprint of Ryland Peters & Small Ltd
20–21 Jockey's Fields, London WC1R 4BW

www.rylandpeters.com

10 9 8 7 6 5 4 3 2 1

A CIP catalogue record for this book is available
from the British Library.

ISBN: 978 1 78249 425 6

Printed in China

Editor: Kate Haxell
Pattern checker: Jemima Bicknell
Designer: Vicky Rankin
Photographer: Penny Wincer
Stylist: Jo Sawkins
Illustrator: Stephen Dew

Art director: Sally Powell
Production controller: Mai-Ling Collyer
Publishing manager: Penny Craig
Publisher: Cindy Richards

SIMPLE CHIC *Crochet*

Contents

Introduction

We love crochet! When we had our yarn store we were very much a knitting AND crochet retailer, not mainly knitting with a little bit of crochet on the side. Some of this was because – quite handily – one of us (Susan) is very much a crochet-er and the other (Karen) a knitter, although we can both switch between the hook and needles if necessary. However, the main reason for our dual yarn-craft approach was the huge increase in interest in the art of crochet. We were inundated week after week with people wanting to learn this lovely craft.

There are a couple of stumbling blocks with crochet though. One is that it does seem to be that bit trickier to learn than knitting. Whether this is because most people have a go at knitting as a child but maybe not crochet, or if it's because crochet is just a bit less intuitive, I'm not sure, but it certainly seems a little harder to get to grips with initially. The other issue is that crochet can have a tendency to look a bit... well... too crocheted. Lacy, great! Textured, great! Overly crochet... hmmm... we're not sure that always works.

So, as you'd expect in a book called *Simple Chic Crochet*, we've tried to create designs that are not only reasonably simple, but also look rather lovely and 'not too crochet'.

Crochet can be just as versatile as knitting and we hope that we've demonstrated that here with a huge variety of garments, accessories and homewares. And in many ways, once you have mastered the basics of crochet, it is much more straightforward than knitting. As well as written patterns we have included charts where appropriate, as we find them very helpful for more complicated designs – you can see exactly where each stitch is supposed to go, which can really help you visualise how everything comes together.

If you are a total beginner, start with one of the blankets, either the camping throw (see page 70) or the bedrunner (see page 52), or if you'd prefer a smaller project, the hot water bottle cover (see page 60) is super-simple, too. There are lots of easy-to-read instructions on techniques you'll need at the back of the book, and don't forget to check out online resources or our own website, www.mrsmoon.co.uk, for videos. One word of warning, make sure you know whether you are watching US or UK tutorials; some of the same stitch names actually describe different stitches, which can be very confusing!

We hope you are inspired by our designs; we've loved creating them and hope that you do, too!

Susan and Karen xxx

CHAPTER 1

To Wear

The idea of crochet garments might evoke scary thoughts of frilly bed jackets and terrible tabards, but actually crochet can be used to make elegant, easy-to-wear items that will become wardrobe staples. And as crochet is so easy to work, the projects in this chapter will grow encouragingly quickly.

GRANNY SQUARE *Coatigan*

When I was planning this fabulous cardi/coat, I was thinking about how garments made of granny squares (or actually any crochet), can be amazing or slightly mad... I hope that I've achieved the amazing category here! This coat swings out beautifully when you walk because of the way it has been constructed, and it has three-quarter-length bell sleeves to give it a sophisticated edge. The coatigan is super-simple to create because you just need a lot of the squares! Once you've made them all, sew them together as shown, then add the all-important collar and front band that finish it off beautifully.

Yarn

Mrs Moon Plump DK (80% superfine merino wool, 20% baby alpaca) double knitting (light-worsted-weight) yarn, 50g (1¾oz), 115m (125yd) skeins

3(4) skeins in Rhubarb Crumble (A)

3(4) skeins in Cherry Pie (B)

15(19) skeins in Blueberry Muffin (C)

Hook and equipment

4mm (US F/5 or G/6) crochet hook

Size

To fit: S/M(M/L)

Finished measurements

Chest: 88(130)cm (34½(51)in)

Length (nape to hem) (including border but not collar): 85(85)cm (34(34)in)

Tension

Each square measures 10.5cm (4¼in) using 4mm (US F/5 or G/6) crochet hook

Abbreviations

PUFF = [yrh, into st, yrh, pull back through st] 3 times, yrh, pull through all 7 loops, to secure puff yrh, pull through loop on hook.

PUFF1 = This is a puff at the beginning of the round, the ch2 counts as one stitch so you work this as a puff but work two instead of three reps (5 loops on hook), yrh and pull through to secure.

See also page 114

SQUARE

Colour 1 is A or B, colour 2 is the one not used, colour 3 is C.

S/M Make 40 squares with A as colour 1, and 40 with B as colour 1.

M/L Make 55 squares with A as colour 1, and 55 with B as colour 1.

In colour 1, ch5 and join with a sl st to form a ring.

Round 1: Ch3 (counts as 1tr), work 15 more tr into ring, join rnd with a sl st into top of ch 3, fasten off colour 1. *(16 sts)*

Round 2: Join colour 2 to any tr from rnd 1, ch2 (counts as 1htr), PUFF1 into same space, work 1 PUFF into next tr and into every tr to end of rnd, join rnd with a sl st into top of ch 2, fasten off colour 2. *(16 puffs)*

Round 3: Join C to any space between puffs, ch3 (counts as 1tr), tr3tog into same space, yrh and pull through to secure, ch1, *tr4tog into next space between puffs, yrh and pull through to secure, ch1; rep from * to end of rnd, finishing with a sl st into top of ch 3.

Round 4: Sl st into next ch 1 space (this is where you need to start this rnd; you may need to sl st twice to do this neatly), into this ch 1 space work (ch3 (counts as 1tr), 2tr, ch2, 3tr) for corner, do not ch1, *3htr into next space, 3dc into foll space, 3htr into next space, ** and into next space work a corner (3tr, ch2, 3tr); rep from * twice more and then work one final rep, finishing at **, join with a sl st to top of ch 3, do not fasten off.

Round 5 (dc round): Ch1, 1dc into same space, 1dc into each of next 2tr, work 3dc into ch 2 corner space, cont working 1dc into every st, and 3dc into every corner space around, finish rnd by joining with a sl st to top of first dc, fasten off.

TO MAKE UP

You can sew the squares (and the seams) together. However, I have crocheted them together by slip stitching them (see page 123). I find this quicker and easier as I am very bad at sewing; it is also easy to pull back if you go wrong.

To join the squares, first arrange them (see diagrams on page 12). Right sides together and slip stitching through the back loops only, join squares to form long strips. Then join the strips together.

Size S/M — Back / Shoulder / Front / Side chart:

		B	B	B	B		
		B	B	B	B		
		B	B	B	B		
		B	B	B	B		
		B	B	B	B		
		B	B	B	B		
		B	B	B	B		
		SH			SH		
		F			F		
S	F					F	S
S	F					F	S
S	F					F	S
S	F					F	S
S	F					F	S
S	F					F	S

Sleeves (SL):

SL	SL	SL
SL	SL	SL
SL	SL	SL
SL	SL	SL

Size M/L — Back / Shoulder / Front / Side chart:

		B	B	B	B	B	B		
		B	B	B	B	B	B		
		B	B	B	B	B	B		
		B	B	B	B	B	B		
		B	B	B	B	B	B		
		B	B	B	B	B	B		
		B	B	B	B	B	B		
		SH	SH			SH	SH		
		F	F			F	F		
S	F	F					F	F	S
S	F	F					F	F	S
S	F	F					F	F	S
S	F	F					F	F	S
S	F	F					F	F	S
S	F	F					F	F	S

Sleeves (SL):

SL	SL	SL
SL	SL	SL
SL	SL	SL
SL	SL	SL

Size S/M

Alternate the colour centres throughout.

Back (B): Lay out a rectangle four squares wide and seven squares long.

Shoulder (SH): Add one square at each end of the top row of four squares.

Front (F): Attach a strip of seven squares lengthways to each shoulder.

Side panels (S): Attach a strip of six squares to each front panel, aligning the bottom edge of the strip with the bottom edge of the front.

Fold the coatigan in half across the middle of the shoulder squares, so that the bottom edges of the back and the front/side pieces match. Join the top two squares of each side panel to the aligning squares on the back (these will be the second and third ones down from the top). Leave the lower part of each side seam open as a split.

Sleeves (SL): Lay out a rectangle four squares wide and three squares long. It's easiest to fit the sleeve into the opening before joining the underarm seam. On the wrong side, join the sleeve squares to the top of the side panel, the single front square, the shoulder square and the topmost back square. Then join the underarm seam.

Size M/L

Alternate the colour centres throughout.

Back (B): Lay out a rectangle six squares wide and seven squares long.

Shoulder (SH): Add two squares at each end of the top row of six squares.

Front (F): Attach two strips of seven squares lengthways to each shoulder.

Side panels (S): Attach a strip of six squares to each front panel, aligning the bottom edge of the strip with the bottom edge of the front.

Fold the coatigan in half across the middle of the shoulder squares, so that the bottom edges of the back and the front/side pieces match. Join the top two squares of each side panel to the aligning squares on the back (these will be the second and third ones down from the top). Leave the lower part of each side seam open as a split.

Sleeves (SL): Lay out a rectangle four squares wide and three squares long. It's easiest to fit the sleeve into the opening before joining the underarm seam. On the wrong side, join the sleeve squares to the top of the side panel, the single front square, the shoulder square and the topmost back square. Then join the underarm seam.

EDGING

Round 1: Using C, work a rnd of dc all the way around the edge of the coat, working 3dc into every corner st (at the bottom edge of each split and at the bottom edge of each side of the front opening), and at each side of the back of the neck (where the front joins the back) and at the top of the split on the side seam work dc3tog as a decrease around the corner.

Rep rnd 1 once more.

Round 3: Work a further rnd of dc just around inside of opening, working dc3tog either side of back neck, fasten off.

COLLAR

Row 4: Using C, work dc around neck (left SH square, two squares of back neck and right SH square), working dc3tog in corners as for edging, turn.

Row 5: Ch1, 1dc into same space and 1dc into every st to end, working dc3tog in corners, turn.

Rep row 5 twice more.

Row 8: Work dc into every st, do not work dc3tog in the corners, turn.

Row 9: Ch3 (counts as 1tr), 1tr into next dc and into each st to end of row, increasing by working 3tr into each corner st, turn.

Rep row 9, 6 times more.

Row 10: Neaten edge of collar with a row of dc starting at the edge of the collar (where it meets the button band) and working evenly up the edge (as a general rule work 2dc down the side of each tr), then work along the top and down the other edge, working 3dc into each front collar point and back neck corners, fasten off.

LEFT-HAND BUTTON BAND

Row 1: Join C to bottom LH corner, ch1 (does not count as st), 1dc into same place, 1dc into every st up to st before the collar starts, turn.

Row 2: Ch1 (does not count as st), 1dc into same place, 1dc into every st to end of row, turn.

Rep row 2, 3 times more.

Fasten off.

RIGHT-HAND BUTTON BAND

Row 1: Join C to st next to collar at top of RH edge, ch1 (does not count as st), 1dc into same place, 1dc into every st to bottom, turn.

Row 2: Ch1 (does not count as st), 1dc into same place, 1dc into every st to end of row, turn.

Rep row 2, 3 times more.

Fasten off.

Weave in ends (see page 125).
Block coatigan following instructions on ball band.

Making squares

I find it easier to make all the circles first (rounds 1–3), and then work rounds 4–5; I guess I get into a rhythm. I also weave in the ends as I go, as this can become an almost insurmountable task if left to the end…

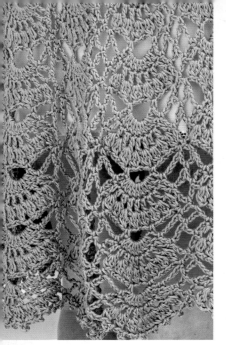

CROCHET *Skirt*

Crochet is, for many garments, quite tricky compared to its close cousin, knitting. Garments just tend to work better with the close fabric that knitting creates... I spend quite a lot of time trying to make my designs look not 'too crochet'! However, the crochet skirt is the big exception! Knitted skirts can be heavy and cumbersome. Crochet creates gorgeous shapes and lace that swings fabulously and really flatters the feminine form. So, here is my first crochet skirt. I'm so pleased with it. It sits on the hips and has no tricky openings to deal with, and it gradually flares out with simple increases in the lace pattern. I urge you to give it a go... your friends will be begging you for one!

Yarn

Cascade Ultra Pima (100% pima cotton) double knitting (sport-weight) yarn, 100g (3½oz), 200m (220yd) skeins

5(6:7) skeins in Taupe 3759

Hook and equipment

3.75mm (US F/5) crochet hook

Large tapestry needle

Size

To fit: S(M:L)

Finished measurements

Waist: 78(83:89)cm (30¾(32½:35)in)

Length (waistband to hem): 49cm (19½in)

Waistband depth: 6cm (2¼in)

Tension

14 sts and 8 rows over tr sts in waistband using 3.75mm (US F/5) crochet hook

Abbreviations

See page 114

SKIRT

Ch112(120:128), join with a sl st to form a ring, being careful not to twist the chain; this is the most difficult part of this project!

Round 1: Ch1, 1dc into same place (this is a bit tricky as it is where the chain joins; if you find it easier you can add an extra st to the base chain), 1dc into every ch to end of rnd, join with a sl st to first dc made, do not turn. *(112(120:128) sts)*

Round 2 (eyelet rnd): Ch1, 1dc into same place, 1dc into next st, *ch2, miss 1 st, 1dc into each of next 4 sts; rep from * around, finishing with 1 dc into each of last 4(3:1) sts, join with a sl st to first dc, do not turn.

Small size only

Round 3 (increase rnd): (This rnd starts in the middle of the back: work 1tr into every ch2 space or st.) Ch3 (counts as 1tr), work 1tr into each of next 23 tr or ch 2 spaces, 2tr into next st, 1tr into each of next 6 sts, 2tr into next st, 1tr in each of next 49 sts, 2tr into next st, 1tr into each of next 6 tr, 2tr into next st, 1tr into each of next 23 sts, join rnd with a sl st to top of ch3, do not turn. *(116 sts)*

Check fit

Round 3 is the start of the waistband so it is worth checking to see if you can get it over your hips! Though it will loosen up a bit, if it feels too tight either go up a size or try a larger hook.

Medium size only

Round 3 (increase rnd): (This rnd starts in the middle of the back: work 1tr into every ch2 space or st.) Ch3 (counts as 1tr), work 1tr into each of next 24 sts, 2tr into next st, 1tr into each of foll 8 sts, 2tr into next st, 1tr into each of next 51 sts, 2tr into next st, 1tr into each of next 8 sts, 2tr into next st, 1tr into each of foll 24 sts, join rnd with a sl st to top of ch3, do not turn. *(124 sts)*

Large size only

Round 3 (increase rnd): (This rnd starts in the middle of the back: work 1tr into every ch2 space or st.) Ch3 (counts as 1tr), work 1tr into each of next 25 sts, 2tr into next st, 1tr into each of next 10 sts, 2tr into foll st, 1tr into each of next 54 sts, 2tr into next st, 1tr into each of next 10 sts, 2tr into next st, 1tr into each of next 24 sts, join rnd with a sl st top of ch3, do not turn. *(132 sts)*

All sizes

Round 4: Ch3 (counts as 1tr), 1tr into every st to first tr of 2 tr increase, 2tr into first of these tr, 1tr into next tr and every st to next 2 tr increase, 1tr into first of these tr and 2tr into next one, 1tr into next tr and every st to next 2 tr increase, 2tr into first of these tr, 1tr into next tr and every st to final 2 tr increase, 1tr into first of these tr and 2tr into next tr, 1tr into next st and every st to end of rnd, join with a sl st to top of ch3, do not turn. *(120(128:136) sts)*

Rounds 5–6: Rep rnd 4, do not turn. *(128(136:144) sts)*
The waistband is finished. Round 6 is first rnd shown on chart (see page 17).

Round 7 (first lace rnd): Ch1, 1dc into same place, *ch3, miss 1 st (be careful not to miss two sts as they are quite difficult to see), 1dc into next st; rep from * finishing with ch3, join rnd with sl st to first dc.

Round 8: Sl st into next ch 3 space, ch1, 1dc into same space, ch3, 1dc into next ch 3 space, 4 tr into foll ch 3 space, *1dc into next ch 3 space, ch3, 1dc into next ch 3 space, ch3, 1dc into foll ch 3 space, 4tr into next ch 3 space; rep from * finishing in last ch 3 space with 1dc, ch1, 1tr into top of first dc made in this rnd.

Round 9: Ch1, 1dc into top of tr, ch3, 1dc into next ch 3 space, *(1tr, ch1) into each of next 3 tr, 1tr into 4th tr, 1dc into next ch 3 space, ch3, 1dc into next ch 3 space; rep from * to end of rnd, finishing with a sl st to top of first dc made.

Round 10: Sl st into next ch 3 space, ch1, 1dc into same place, *ch2, tr3tog in the ch1 space between the 1st and 2nd tr, ch1, (tr3tog, ch1) into next ch 1 space, tr3tog into next ch 1 space, ch2, 1dc into ch 3 space; rep from * finishing with ch2, sl st into first dc made.

Round 11: Sl st into the ch 2 space, ch1, 1dc into same space, *ch4, miss 1 tr3tog, 1dc into ch 1 space, ch4, miss next tr3tog, 1dc into next ch 1 space, ch4, miss final tr3tog, 1dc into ch 2 space, ch4, 1 dc into next ch 2 space; rep from * to end of rnd, finishing with 1dc into last ch 2 space, ch2, 1tr into first dc made.

Round 12: Ch1, 1dc into top of tr, ch4, 1dc into next ch 4 space, *5tr into next ch 4 space (this should be directly over first group of rnd 8), 1dc into next ch 4 space, ch4, 1dc into next ch 4 space, ch4, 1dc into foll ch 4 space; rep from * to end of rnd, finishing with 1dc into last ch 4 space, ch2, 1tr into first dc made.

Round 13: Ch1, 1dc into top of tr, ch4, 1dc into next ch 4 space, *(1tr, ch1) into each of next 4 tr, 1tr into final tr, 1dc into next ch 4 space, ch4, 1dc into next ch 4 space; rep from * to end of rnd, finishing with 1tr into last tr of group of 5 tr, sl st to first dc made.

Round 14: Sl st twice into next ch 4 space, ch1, 1dc into same space, ch2,*(tr3tog, ch1) into each of first three ch 1 spaces, tr3tog in fourth ch 1 space, ch2, 1dc into ch 4 space, ch2; rep from * finishing after final group of tr3tog with ch2, join with sl st to first dc made.

Round 15: Sl st into next ch 2 space, ch1, 1dc into same place, *ch4, miss first tr3tog, 1dc into next ch 1 space, ch4, miss two tr3tog, 1dc into next ch 1 space, ch4, miss final tr3tog, 1dc into ch 2 space, ch4, 1dc into next ch 2 space; rep from * finishing with 1dc in last ch 2 space, ch2, 1tr into first dc made.

Rounds 16–18: Rep rnds 12–14.

Round 19: Rep rnd 15. If this rnd feels a bit tight, you can replace all the ch4 with ch5.

Round 20: Ch1, 1dc into top of tr, ch5, 1dc into next ch space, *7tr into foll ch space, 1dc into next ch space, ch5, 1dc into next ch space, ch5, 1dc into next ch space; rep from * finishing with 1dc in last ch 2 space, ch2, 1tr into first dc made.

Round 21: Ch1, 1dc into top of tr, ch5, 1dc into next ch 5 space, *(1tr, ch1) into each of next 6 tr, 1tr in final tr, 1dc into next ch 5 space, ch5, 1dc into next ch 5 space; rep from * to end of rnd, after final tr join rnd with a sl st to first dc made.

Round 22: Sl st twice into next ch 5 space, ch1, 1dc into same place, ch2, *(tr3tog, ch1) into each of next five ch 1 spaces between tr, tr3tog in last ch 1 space, ch2, 1dc into next ch 5 space, ch2; rep from * finishing with ch2, join rnd with a sl st to first dc made.

Round 23: Sl st into next ch 2 space, ch1, 1dc into same place, *ch6, miss two tr3tog, 1dc into next ch 1 space, ch6, miss two tr3tog, 1dc into next ch 1 space, ch6, miss final two tr3tog, 1dc into ch 2 space, ch6, 1dc into next ch 2 space; rep from * finishing with 1dc into last ch 2 space, ch3, 1tr into first dc made.

Rounds 24–26: Rep rnds 20–22.

Round 27: Rep rnd 23.

Round 28: Ch1, 1dc into same place, ch6, 1dc into next ch 6 space, *9tr into next ch 6 space, 1dc into next ch 6 space, ch6, 1dc into foll ch 6 space, ch6, 1dc into next ch 6 space; rep from * finishing with 1dc into last ch 6 space, ch3, 1tr into first dc made.

Round 29: Ch1, 1dc into top of tr, ch6, 1dc into next ch 6 space, *(1tr, ch1) into each of next 8tr, 1tr into last tr, 1dc into ch 6 space, ch6, 1dc into next ch 6 space; rep from * finishing after final tr with a sl st into first dc made.

Round 30: Sl st twice into next ch 6 space, ch1, 1dc into same space, ch2, *work (tr3tog, ch1) into each of next seven ch1 spaces, tr3tog in last ch 1 space, ch2, 1dc into next ch 6 space, ch2; rep from * finishing with ch2, sl st into first dc made.

Round 31: Sl st into next ch 2 space, ch1, 1dc into same place, *ch6, miss three tr3tog, 1dc into next ch 1 space, ch6, miss two tr3tog, 1dc into next ch 1 space, ch6, miss final three tr3tog, 1dc into ch 2 space, ch6, 1dc into next ch 2 space; rep from * finishing with 1dc into last ch 2 space, ch3, 1tr into first dc made.

Rep rnds 28–31 until skirt is required length, ending after rnd 29. I have worked some silver thread along with the pima cotton in the last full repeat to give it a bit of sparkle.

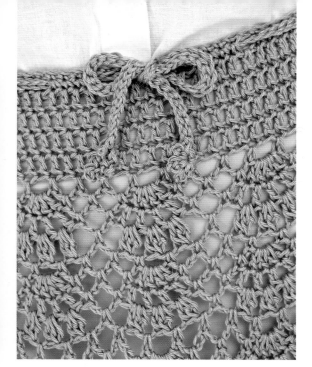

Final round (picot round): Sl st twice into next ch 6 space, ch1, 1dc into same space, ch2, *work (tr3tog, ch3, sl st into the top of tr3tog, ch1) into each of next seven ch1 spaces, (tr3tog, ch3, sl st into the top of tr3tog) in last ch 1 space, ch2, 1dc into next ch 6 space, ch2; rep from * finishing with ch2, sl st into first dc made.
Fasten off.

DRAWSTRING

Using pima cotton and sparkle yarn double, ch181, 1dc into 2nd ch from hook and into each ch to end, do not fasten off, *ch3, sl st into 3rd of ch 3, ch3, sl st into same place as first sl st; rep from * 3 times more to make a flower, join rnd with a sl st, fasten off.
Starting in the middle of the skirt front, thread the drawstring through the eyelets made on row 2. When you have woven it through, make another flower as above and stitch to the plain end.

TO MAKE UP

Weave in ends (see page 125).

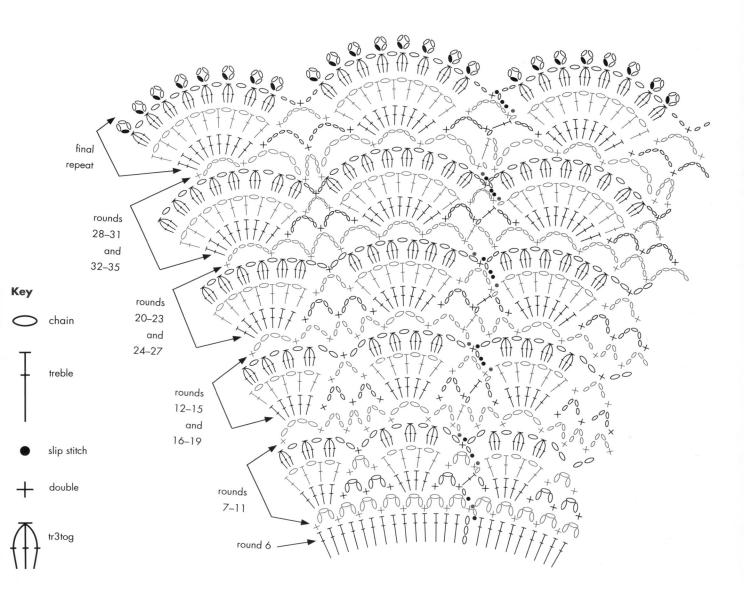

final repeat

rounds 28–31 and 32–35

rounds 20–23 and 24–27

rounds 12–15 and 16–19

rounds 7–11

round 6

Key

⬭ chain

┬ treble

● slip stitch

+ double

⋔ tr3tog

LACE *Sun Top*

This pretty, lacy top is a great way to try out pineapple lace, which is something every crocheter – in my personal opinion, of course – should try! Pineapple lace is traditionally viewed as rather old-fashioned and associated with doilies or antimacassars, but it is a beautiful stitch and can be used to wonderful effect in the modern world. This sun top looks great over a plain cami and is a beautiful addition to a summer wardrobe. I would count this as one of the slightly trickier projects in the book, but because of the relative complexity of the lace, I've kept the construction of the top very basic; shaping is achieved by making the pineapples larger. There is a chart as well as the written pattern to help you work the lace.

Yarn

Cascade Ultra Pima (100% pima cotton) double knitting (sport-weight) yarn, 100g (3½oz), 200m (220yd) skeins
3(4:4:5) skeins in Buttercup 3748

Hook and equipment

3.5mm (US E/4) crochet hook
Large tapestry needle

Size

To fit: XS(S:M:L)
Finished measurements
Chest: 66(85:104:123)cm (26(33½:41:48½)in)
Length (excluding straps): 43(43:43:43)cm (17(17:17:17)in)

Tension

One small pineapple motif (not including chains) measures 5cm (2in) long by 4cm (1½in) wide at widest point

Abbreviations

See page 114

BACK AND FRONT

(Make 2; worked from the top down)
Ch66(82:98:114) loosely.
Row 1: 1dc into 2nd ch from hook and into every ch to end, turn. *(65(81:97:113) sts)*
Row 2: Ch1, 1dc into same place, 1dc into every st to end, turn.
Row 3 (first row shown on chart): Rep row 2.
Row 4 (lace pattern): Ch1, 1dc into same place, ch3, miss 1 st, 1dc into next st, ch3, miss next st, 1dc into foll st, *ch5, miss 3 sts, 1dc into next st, ch5, miss 3 sts**, 1dc into foll st, [ch3, miss 1 st, 1dc into foll st] 4 times; rep from * to last 5 ch finishing at **, then 1dc, ch3, miss 1 st, 1dc into next st, ch3, miss next st, 1dc into last st, turn.
Row 5: Ch4, 1dc into first ch 3 space, ch3, 1dc into next ch 3 space, *ch5, (miss the ch 5 from row 4), 1tr into next dc, ch5, (miss next ch 5), 1dc into foll ch 3 space, ch3, 1dc into next ch 3 space**, ch3, 1dc into next ch 3 space, ch3, 1dc into final ch 3 space; rep from * to end of row, finishing at **, then ch1, 1tr into dc (at the start of row 4), turn.
Row 6: Ch1, 1dc into top of tr, ch3, 1dc into the ch 3 space, *ch5, (1tr, ch1, 1tr) into next tr, ch5, 1dc into next ch 3 space, ch3**, 1dc into foll ch 3 space, ch3, 1dc into last ch 3 space; rep from * to end of row, finishing at ** then working last dc into ch 4 space (turning ch from row 5), turn.
Row 7: Ch4, 1dc into first ch 3 space, *ch5, (1tr, ch1, 1tr, ch1, 1tr, ch1, 1tr, ch1, 1tr) into ch 1 space between 2 tr, ch5, 1dc into next ch 3 space, **ch3, 1dc into foll ch 3 space; rep from * finishing at ** then ch1, 1tr into last dc from row 6, turn.
Row 8: Ch8, miss ch 5, *(1dc, ch3) into each of next 4 tr, 1dc into final tr of group, ch5, 1tr into next ch 3 space, ch5; rep from * to end of row, finishing with ch5, 1tr into ch 4 space, turn.
Row 9: Ch8, *1dc into first ch 3 space of group, (ch3, 1dc) into each of next 3 ch spaces, ch5, miss ch 5, 1tr into the tr, ch5; rep from * to end of row, finishing with ch5, 1tr into ch 8 space, turn.

After these rows the basic pattern remains the same except that the size of each pineapple increases by one row. If preferred, the same end result can be achieved by going up to a 3.75mm (US F/5) hook and repeating the pattern above.

Row 19: Ch4 (counts as 1tr, ch1), (1tr, ch1, 1tr, ch1, 1tr) into first tr, ch6, *1dc into first ch 3 space, ch3, 1dc into next ch 3 space, ch6, (1tr, ch1, 1tr, ch1, 1tr, ch1, 1tr, ch1, 1tr) into ch 1 space between tr, ch6; rep from * to end of row, finishing with ch6, (1tr, ch1, 1tr, ch1, 1tr, ch1, 1tr) into top of ch 3, turn.

Row 20: Ch1, (1dc into tr, ch3) into each of next 3 tr, 1 dc into next tr, *ch6, 1tr into ch 3 space, ch6, (1dc, ch3) into each of next 5 tr, 1dc into final tr of group; rep from * to end of row, finishing with 1tr into last ch 3 space, ch6, 1dc into next tr, ch3, 1dc into foll tr, ch3, 1dc into next tr, ch3, 1dc into the ch 4 space, turn.

Row 21: Ch4, 1dc into first ch 3 space, (ch3, 1dc) into each of next two ch 3 spaces, * ch6, (miss the ch 6 space), 1tr into next tr, ch6, (miss next ch 6), (1dc, ch3) into each of next 4 ch 3 spaces, 1dc into final ch 3 space of group; rep from * to end of row, finishing after final ch 6 with 1dc into next ch 3 space, ch3, 1dc into next ch 3 space, ch3,1dc into final ch 3 space, ch2, 1tr into the dc, turn.

Row 22: Ch1, 1dc into first tr, ch3, 1dc into next ch 3 space, ch3, 1dc into foll ch 3 space, *ch6, 1tr into next tr, ch6, (1dc, ch3) into each of next two ch 3 spaces, 1dc into final ch 3 space; rep from * to end of row, finishing after final ch 6 with 1dc into next ch 3 space, ch3, 1dc into next ch 3 space, ch3, 1dc into the ch 4 space, turn.

Row 23: Ch4, (counts as 1 tr, ch 1), 1dc into first ch 3 space, ch3, dc into next ch 3 space, *ch6, (1tr, ch1, 1tr) into next tr, ch6, (1dc, ch3) into each of next two ch 3 spaces, 1dc into final ch 3 space; rep from * to end of row, finishing after final ch 6 with 1dc into next ch 3 space, ch3, 1dc into next ch 3 space, ch2, 1tr into final dc, turn.

Row 24: Ch4, 1dc into first ch 3 space, ch6, *(1tr, ch1, 1tr, ch1, 1tr, ch1, 1tr, ch1, 1tr) into ch1 space between next 2 tr, ch6, *1dc into first ch 3 space, ch3, 1dc into next ch 3 space, ch6; rep from * to end of row, finishing after final ch 6 with 1dc into final ch 3 space, ch1, 1tr into the ch 4 space, turn.

Row 25: Ch9, *(1dc, ch3) into each of next 5 tr, 1dc into final tr of group, ch6, 1tr into next ch 3 space, ch6; rep from * to end of row, finishing after final ch 6 with 1tr into ch 4 space, turn.

Row 26: Ch9, *(1dc, ch3) into each of next four ch 3 spaces, 1dc into final ch 3 space of group, ch6, 1tr into next tr, ch6; rep from * to end of row, finishing after first ch 6 with 1tr into ch 9 space, turn.

Row 10: Ch3, 1tr into same place, *ch5, (1dc, ch3) into each of next two ch 3 spaces, 1dc into final ch 3 space of group, ch5, miss ch 5, (1tr, ch1, 1tr) into the tr; rep from * to end of row, finishing with ch5, 2tr into 3rd ch of ch 8, turn.

Row 11: Ch4 (counts as1tr, ch1), (1tr, ch1, 1tr) into first tr, ch5, *1dc into first ch 3 space, ch3, 1dc into next ch 3 space, ch5, (1tr, ch1, 1tr, ch1, 1tr, ch1, 1tr, ch1, 1tr) into ch 1 space between tr, ch5; rep from * to end of row, finishing with ch5, (1tr, ch1, 1tr, ch1, 1tr) into top of ch 3, turn.

Row 12: Ch1, (1dc into tr, ch3) into each of next two tr, 1 dc into next tr, *ch5, 1tr into the ch 3 space, ch5, (1dc, ch3) into each of next 4 tr, 1dc into final tr of group; rep from * to end of row, finishing with 1tr into last ch 3 space, ch5, 1dc into next tr, ch3, 1dc into foll tr, ch3, 1dc into the ch 4 space, turn.

Rows 13–18: Rep rows 5–10 once more.

The rows above establish the pattern, see the chart for a guide for this part.

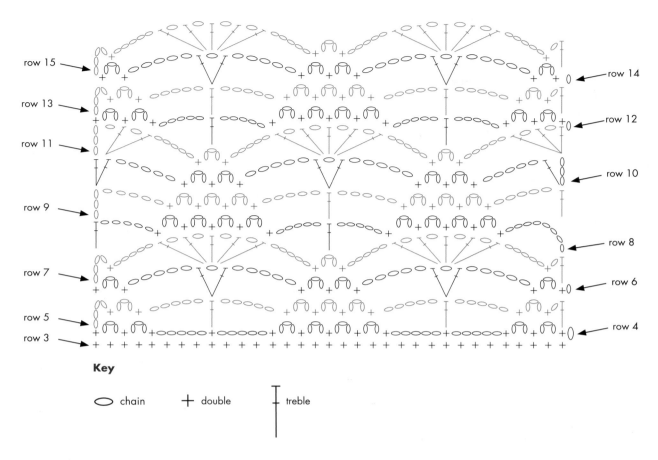

row 15
row 13
row 11
row 9
row 7
row 5
row 3

row 14
row 12
row 10
row 8
row 6
row 4

Key

⬭ chain   + double   ⊺ treble

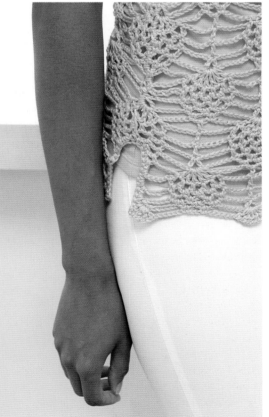

Row 27: Ch9, *(1dc, ch3) into each of next three ch 3 spaces, 1dc into final ch 3 space of group, ch6, 1tr into next tr, ch6; rep from * to end of row, finishing after first ch 6 with 1tr into ch 9 space, turn.

Row 28: Ch3, 1tr into same place, *ch6, (1dc, ch3) into each of next two ch 3 spaces, 1dc into final ch 3 space, **ch6, (1tr, ch1, 1tr) into next tr; rep from * to end of row, finishing at ** then ch6, 2tr into 3rd ch of ch 9, turn.

Row 29 onwards: Rep rows 19–28 twice more, or until the top is the required length.

Final row: Rep row 19, fasten off.

TO MAKE UP

Weave in ends (see page 125).

Press before you sew up the top.

Place the front and back right sides together and seam up both sides; you can do this by either using dc or oversewing. Try the top on, work out how long you want the shoulder straps to be and then make a ch slightly longer than this for each strap (I have made a ch of 90). Work 3 rows of dc into the ch to complete each strap. Sew the straps into place.

CHUNKY *Cardigan*

Snuggly, chic, lightweight and generally gorgeous, this cardigan will become invaluable as soon as you have finished it. The design is kept simple and rather like the Easy Crochet Sweater (see page 31), begins at the top, increasing at the raglan sleeves and then continuing down through the body. It has beautiful, slightly bell-shaped sleeves and a proper collar that gives the cardigan a professional finish. This is really not at all difficult to crochet, and a great place to start if you are creating a garment for the first time. The sleeves are crocheted in the round, but this is very simple to do and shouldn't put you off.

Yarn

Mrs Moon Plump (80% superfine merino wool, 20% baby alpaca) super-chunky (super-bulky) yarn, 100g (3½oz), 70m (76yd) skeins

7(8:9) skeins in Cherry Pie

Hook and equipment

12mm (US O/17) crochet hook

Large tapestry needle

Size

To fit: S(M:L)

Finished measurements

Chest: 96(104:112)cm (37¾(41:44)in)

Neck to underarm: 28(31.5:35)cm (11(12½:13¾)in)

Length (nape to hem): 57cm (22½in)

Sleeve (underarm seam): 34cm (13½in)

Tension

6 sts and 3.25 rows over 10cm (4in) using 12mm (US O/17) crochet hook

Abbreviations

See page 114

BODY

Ch36.

Row 1: 1tr into 4th ch from hook, 1tr into each of next 4 ch, (1tr, ch1, 1tr) into next ch, 1tr into each of next 3 ch, (1tr, ch1, 1tr) into next ch, 1tr into each of next 12 ch, (1tr, ch1, 1tr) into next ch, 1tr into each of next 3 ch, (1tr, ch1, 1tr) into next ch, 1tr into each of next 6 ch, turn. *(38 sts)*

The (1tr, ch1, 1tr) groups mark the four points of increase around the raglan sleeves.

Row 2: Ch3 (counts as 1 tr), 1tr into each of next 6 tr, (1tr, ch1, 1tr) into the ch 1 space, 1tr into each of next 5 tr, (1tr, ch1, 1tr) into next ch 1 space, 1tr into each of next 14 tr, (1tr, ch1, 1tr) into next ch 1 space, 1tr into each of next 5 tr, (1tr, ch1, 1tr) into next ch 1 space, 1tr into each of next 7 sts (the 7th tr is into top of the tch), turn. *(46 sts)*

Rows 3–8: Work in patt as set, increasing 4 times in every row at the ch 1 space from the previous row, turn. *(94 sts)*

Sizes M(L)

Work 1(2) more rows in patt. *(102(110) sts)*

Sizing the cardigan

The beauty of this pattern is that you can try it on as you go, allowing you to get to the right point to separate out for the sleeves (if the size you are working does not fit!).

SHAPE ARMHOLES

Lay the body flat and tie a loop of contrast yarn through the ch 1 spaces on each side of both armholes; this makes it easier to see what you are doing. You are going to continue to work the body while leaving the two sets of sleeve sts unworked.

Row 1: Ch3 (counts as 1 tr), 1tr into each of next 13(14:15) sts, miss next ch 1 space, miss next 19(21:23) sts (these sts are for the first sleeve and will be returned to later), miss next ch 1 space, work 1tr in next tr (first underarm joined), 1tr into each of next 27(29:31) sts (along the back), miss next ch1 space, miss next 19(21:23) sts (second sleeve sts), miss next ch1 space, work 1tr in next tr (second underarm joined) 1tr into each of next 13(14:15) sts, working last tr into top of the tch, turn. *(56(60:64) sts)*

Rows 2–11: Ch3 (counts as 1 tr), 1tr into every tr in previous row, working last st into top of the tch, fasten off. *(56(60:64) sts)*
You can, of course, make your jacket longer by adding more rows before fastening off if you wish.

SLEEVE

I have decreased several times to bring the sleeves in; the great thing about working in the round in crochet is that you can try the garment on as you go, so check and see whether you want more or fewer decreases.

Round 1: With RS facing, join yarn to the first ch 1 underarm space at back of armhole, ch3 (counts as 1 tr), 1 tr into next 19(21:23) sts and into the last ch 1 space, join rnd with a sl st into top of ch 3, turn. *(21(23:25) sts)*

Round 2: Ch3 (counts as 1 tr), 1tr into every st, join rnd with a sl st into top of ch 3.
Rep rnd 2, 3 more times.

Round 6 (decrease): Ch3 (counts as 1 tr), tr2tog, 1tr into every st to end of rnd, join rnd with a sl st into top of ch 3, turn.

Round 7: Rep rnd 2.

Round 8: Rep rnd 6.

Rounds 9–10: Rep rnd 2.

Round 11: Ch1, 1dc into same place, 1dc into each st to end, join rnd with a sl st into top of first dc, fasten off.
You will have quite a large gap in the underarm because the stitches are quite high. When you have finished you can sew this up.
Rep for second sleeve.

COLLAR

Row 1: With RS facing, join the yarn to corner of right front neck of the cardigan, 1dc into each ch along foundation chain to left front neck corner, turn. *(34 sts)*

Row 2: Ch3 (counts as 1 tr), 1tr into each of next 5 sts, (1tr, ch1, 1tr) into next st, 1tr into each of next 3 tr, (1tr, ch1, 1tr) into next st, 1tr into each of next 12 sts, (1tr, ch1, 1tr) into next st, 1tr into each of next 3 sts, (1tr, ch1, 1tr) into next st, 1tr into each of last 6 sts, turn.
Work as for body for two more rows, working 1 tr into each tr and (1tr, ch1, 1tr) into each ch 1 space, fasten off.

TRIM

Starting in the middle of the back edge of collar, ch1, 1dc into same place, work 1 row of dc around entire edge of cardigan (as a general rule work 2dc into the side of each tr and work 3dc in every corner space): around the collar, down one front edge, around the bottom edge, up the other front edge and around the other edge of collar to first dc, sl st to top of first dc to join, fasten off.

TO MAKE UP

Weave in ends (see page 125).

Substituting yarn

Plump is a very light but warm super-chunky yarn and works perfectly for a big garment. If you do decide to substitute with another yarn, be wary of the density of the fibres – you don't want to be weighed down too much!

SPARKLY *Shrug*

This is so pretty! A shrug is a lovely cover-up for a special summer's evening, or adds a bit of glamour to a wintry night! And although the pattern is lacy, it is not at all difficult. The shrug is made in two rectangles sewn together, so that the lace pattern moves out from the centre. You then simply seam up each end into a tube to make the arms. I have used a sparkly yarn, but any DK-weight yarn would work; a silk mix would be particularly lovely, or a mercerised cotton.

Yarn

Lanas Stop Platino (100% nylon) double knitting (sport-weight) yarn, 50g (1¾oz), 200m (208yd) balls
4(5:5) balls in Black

Hook and equipment

4mm (US F/5 or G/6) crochet hook
Large tapestry needle

Size

To fit: S(M:L)
Finished measurements
Width before sewing for sleeves: 38(43:48)cm (15(17:18¾)in)
Length (along arms): 100(106:112)cm (39½(41¾:44)in)

Tension

Each fan measures approx 5.5cm (2¼in) wide and 3cm (1¼in) high using 4mm (US F/5 or G/6) crochet hook

Abbreviations

PICOT = ch3, sl st into the 3rd ch from hook (if this looks too loose, then sl st into top of the treble the picot is attached to by inserting hook from top to bottom and going through the two strands).
See also page 114

FIRST HALF OF SHRUG

Ch86(98:110) loosely.
Row 1: 1dc into the 2nd ch from hook, *ch5, miss 3 ch, 1dc into next ch; rep from * to end, finishing with 1dc into last ch, turn.
Row 2: Ch5 (counts as 1 tr, ch2), 1dc into ch 5 space, 8tr into next ch 5 space, *1dc into the foll ch 5 space, ch5, 1dc into next ch 5 space, 8 tr into next ch 5 space; rep from * to end of row, finishing with 1dc in final ch 5 space, ch2, 1tr into last dc, turn.
Row 3: Ch1 (does not count as st), 1dc into the first st, *(1tr, 1 picot) into the 1st tr of group of 8 tr, (1tr, 1 picot) into each of next 6 tr, 1tr into the final tr of group, 1dc into the ch 5 space; rep from * finishing with 1dc into the final ch 5 space, turn.
Row 4: Ch8 (counts as 1 tr, ch5), miss 2 picots, *1dc into 3rd picot, ch5, 1dc into 5th picot, ch5, miss 2 picots, 1tr into the dc, ch5, miss 2 picots; rep from * to end of row, finishing by working 1dc into 5th picot of last shell, ch5, miss last 2 picots, 1tr into last dc, turn.
Row 5: Ch5 (counts as 1 tr, ch2), 1dc into 1st ch 5 space, *8tr into next ch 5 space, 1dc into next ch 5 space, ch5, 1dc into next ch 5 space; rep from * to last ch 8 space, 1dc into this space, ch2, 1tr into the 3rd ch of the tch, turn.
Rep rows 3–5 until 17(18:19) reps completed, finishing with row 3.

SECOND HALF OF SHRUG

The second half of the shrug is worked from the base ch of the first half (the base ch will become the centre back), as folls:
With RS of fabric facing, attach yarn to the 1st ch at RH edge and work as for first half of shrug, starting from row 1.

SLEEVES

The sleeves are made by seaming partway up each end of the shrug (which currently looks like a scarf). Sew or dc up from each end through 8 repeats, check fit, and sew more/less as necessary.

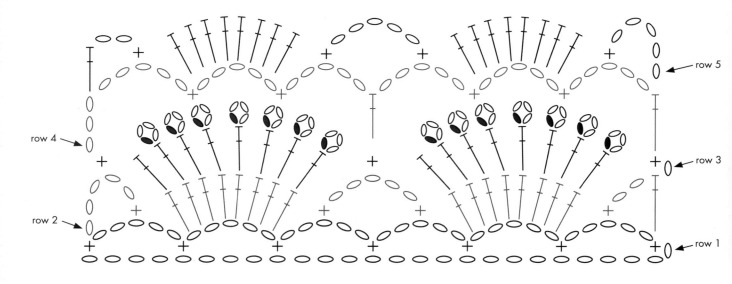

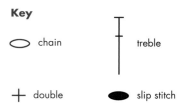

EDGING

Join yarn to top of centre back seam, work 252(288:324) dc evenly around the neck opening, join with a sl st to the first dc made. This is to allow for 21(24:27) fans around the opening.

Round 1: Ch1, 1dc into same place, *ch5, miss 3 sts, 1dc into next st; rep from * to end of rnd, join with a sl st to 1st dc made.

Round 2: Sl st into next ch 5 space, **ch3 (counts as 1 tr), work 7 more tr into same ch 5 space, *1 dc into next ch 5 space, ch5, 1dc into the foll ch 5 space, 8tr into next ch 5 space; rep from * to last two ch 5 spaces, 1dc into next ch 5 space, ch5, 1 dc into last ch 5 space, join rnd with a sl st to top of ch 3.

Round 3: Ch3 (counts as 1 tr), picot, (1tr, picot) into each of next 6 tr, 1tr into the final tr of group, *1dc into next ch 5 space, (1tr, picot) into each of next 7 tr, 1tr into final tr of group; rep from * finishing with 1dc into last ch5 space, join rnd with a sl st to top of ch 3, fasten off.

Round 4: Rejoin yarn to last ch 5 space of rnd 3 (this is where you need to start this rnd), ch8 (counts as 1 tr, ch5), miss first 2 picots, 1dc into 3rd picot, ch5, 1dc into 5th picot, ch5, miss final two picots, *1tr into next dc, (1tr, picot) into each of next 7 tr, 1tr into last tr; rep from * to end of rnd, join with a sl st to 3rd ch of ch 8, fasten off.

Round 5: Miss next ch 5, rejoin yarn in foll ch 5 space (this should lie directly above last fan); rep rnd 2 from **. Rep row 4 once more, fasten off.

TO MAKE UP

Weave in ends (see page 125).

Key

◯ chain   │ treble

+ double   ⬬ slip stitch

TANK *Top*

Tank tops are so useful and versatile, and can get away with being made in all sorts of colours! I've always wanted to create a crochet tank top that is reminiscent of the traditional knitted Fair Isle versions, and I think I've managed it here! If you have never crocheted an actual garment before then this is a good place to start. The rib is very easy to work and the colour patterning is basically granny stripes; it's a very simple design with no tricky shaping.

Yarn

Mrs Moon Plump DK (80% superfine merino wool, 20% baby alpaca) double knitting (light-worsted-weight) yarn, 50g (1¾oz), 115m (125yd) skeins

1(2:2:2) skeins in Gooseberry Fool (A)
1(1:2:2) skeins in Sugared Almond (B)
1(1:2:2) skeins in Pistachio Ice Cream (C)
1(1:2:2) skeins in Peppermint Cream (D)

If you want to make a plain coloured tank top you will need:
4(5:5:6) skeins in colour of your choice

Hooks and equipment

4.5mm (US G/6 or H/8) and 5mm (US H/8 or I/9) crochet hooks
Large tapestry needle

Size

To fit: XS(S:M:L)
Finished measurements
Length (nape to hem, unstretched): 53(56:59:62)cm (21(22¼:23¼:24½)in)
Chest (unstretched): 70(80:90:100)cm (27½(31½:35½:39½)in)
This garment is designed to be fitted and will stretch

Tension

4 x 3tr groups + 1 ch space and 8 rows over 10cm (4in) using 5mm (US H/8 or I/9) crochet hook

Abbreviations

See page 114

BACK

Using 4.5mm (US G/6 or H/8) hook and A, ch56(64:72:80) loosely.

Row 1: Work 2tr into 4th ch from hook, ch1, miss 3 ch, *3tr into next ch, ch1, miss 3 ch; rep from * to end of row, working 3tr into last ch, turn. *(14(16:18:20) 3tr groups)*

Row 2: Using B, ch4 (counts as 1 tr and 1 ch), 3tr into first ch 1 space, *ch1, 3tr into next ch 1 space; rep from * to end of row, finishing with 1 group of 3tr into last ch 1 space, ch1, 1tr into top of ch 3, turn. *(13(15:17:19) 3tr groups)*

Row 3: Using C, ch3 (counts as 1tr), 2tr into first ch 1 space, *ch1, 3tr into next ch 1 space; rep from * to end of row, finishing with 3tr into last ch 4 space, turn. *(14(16:18:20) 3tr groups)*

Work next row in D and keeping colour stripe patt as set (1 row in each of A, B, C, D in turn), rep rows 2–3 until there are 11 rows in total, then change to 5mm (US H/8 or I/9) hook.
Cont in patt until there are 19 rows in total, turn.**
If you want your tank top to be longer, add more rows here, but you must finish with an odd number of rows.

SHAPE ARMHOLES

XS and S sizes only

Row 20: Without changing colour, *1 sl st into each of next 3tr, 1 sl st into next ch 1 space; rep from * once more, change to next colour in stripe patt, ch3 (counts as 1 tr), 2 tr into same ch 1 space; cont in patt until 11(13) groups of 3 tr have been worked, turn.

A perfect fit

I've deliberately made this tank top to finish at the waist and be very fitted. If you want to lengthen it I've noted in the pattern where you can do this, but bear in mind that you may need more yarn.

Checking your tension

I am quite a loose crocheter, so I would really recommend you double-check your tension before you get to the armholes! If you find that you are much tighter, try using a larger hook size or you could consider going up a size.

M and L sizes only
Row 20: Without changing colour, *1 sl st into each of next 3tr, 1 sl st into next ch 1 space; rep from * twice more, change to next colour in stripe patt, ch3 (counts as 1 tr), 2 tr into same ch 1 space; cont in patt until 13(15) groups of 3 tr have been worked, turn.

All sizes
Note: Continue to maintain colour stripe patt as set.
Row 21: Ch4 (counts as 1 tr and 1 ch), 3 tr into first ch 1 space, cont in patt to end of row, finishing with 3tr into last ch 1 space, ch1, 1tr into top of ch 3, turn.
Cont in patt until 13(15:17:19) complete rows have been worked from start of armhole.
Fasten off.

FRONT

Using 4.5mm (US G/6 or H/8) hook and A, ch56(64:72:80) loosely.
Work as for Back to **. If you have made the back longer, then add the same number of extra rows here too.
Left-hand armhole
XS and S sizes only
Row 20 (RS): Without changing colour, *1 sl st into each of next 3tr, 1 sl st into next ch 1 space; rep from * once more, change to next colour in stripe patt, ch3 (counts as 1 tr), 2 tr into same ch 1 space, **ch1, 3tr into next ch 1 space; rep from ** once more (3 groups of 3 tr), turn.
M and L sizes only
Row 20: Without changing colour, *1 sl st into each of next 3tr, 1 sl st into next ch 1 space; rep from * twice more, change to next colour in stripe patt, ch3 (counts as 1 tr), 2 more tr into same ch 1 space, **ch1, 3tr into next ch 1 space; rep from ** once more (3 groups of 3 tr), turn.
All sizes
Row 21: Ch4 (counts as 1 tr and 1 ch), 3tr into ch 1 space, ch1, 3tr into next ch 1 space, ch1, 1tr into top of ch 3, turn.
Row 22: Ch3 (counts as 1 tr), 2tr into ch 1 space, ch1, 3tr into next ch 1 space, ch1, 3tr into ch 4 space, turn.
Rep rows 21–22 until 13(15:17:19) rows have been worked from start of armhole.
Fasten off.

RIGHT-HAND ARMHOLE

Row 20: With RS facing, starting at bottom left of left-hand armhole, miss 6(8:8:10) groups of 3tr on row 19, join yarn into next ch 1 space, ch3 (counts as 1 tr), 2tr into same ch 1 space, ch1, 3tr into next ch 1 space, ch1, 3tr into next ch 1 space, (3 groups of 3 tr), turn.
Row 21: Ch4 (counts as 1 tr and 1 ch), 3tr into ch 1 space, ch1, 3tr into next ch 1 space, ch1, 1tr into top of ch 3, turn.
Row 22: Ch3 (counts as 1 tr), 2tr into ch 1 space, ch1, 3tr into next ch 1 space, ch1, 3tr into ch 4 space, turn.
Rep rows 21–22 until 13(15:17:19) rows have been worked from start of armhole.
Fasten off.

TO MAKE UP

With RS together, sew or crochet up the shoulder seam and then each side seam. I prefer to seam with dc as I find it faster and easier to pull back when I go wrong (also, I am dreadful at sewing).

CROCHET RIB

Using A and 4.5mm (US G/6 or H/8) hook and with RS facing, join the yarn to the bottom LH side corner.
Ch1, 1dc into same space, 1dc into next st and into every st around bottom edge, join with a sl st to first dc (you will be working into the base chain).
Turn work sideways, ch16, dc into 2nd chain from hook and into every ch back to the garment, sl st into each of next two edge dc of the tank top, turn.
*Miss the two edge sl sts and work 1dc into BLO of every dc along the rib section (15 sts), turn.
Ch1, 1dc into BLO of every st back along the rib section to the garment, sl st into each of next two edge dc of the tank top, turn.
Rep from * around bottom edge of tank top. When you reach the end, fasten off. Use the large tapestry needle to join the two ends of the rib by sewing together through the BLO of both ends of the rib.

ARMHOLE TRIM

Using B and 4.5mm (US G/6 or H/8) hook and with RS facing, join yarn to underarm seam.
Work 1dc into every tr and 1 dc into every ch 1 space, working 2dctog around the corner, cont working evenly around the armhole, working 2dctog around the bottom corner.
As a general rule, when working along the sides of tr, work 2dc into each tr.

NECK TRIM

Work as for the armholes, starting at the middle of the back and remembering to work 2dctog into each of the 4 corners.
Fasten off.

Weave in ends (see page 125).

EASY CROCHET *Sweater*

I love a sloppy sweater that can be thrown over anything if it gets a bit chilly, but is still lovely and light, and looks great. This is one such item; it is so light-weight, but incredibly snuggly, and happens to look rather fabulous! The open-ness of the stitches gives it a slightly retro punk-rock feel, which is great too! This sweater is crocheted in the round, which means that there are no seams to sew up at the end (and that is surely always a good thing?!). Crocheting in the round is very simple and nowhere near as complicated as knitting in the round can sometimes seem, so even if you are a novice crocheter, I would thoroughly recommend giving this sweater a go!

Yarn

Mrs Moon Plump (80% superfine merino wool, 20% baby alpaca) super-chunky (super-bulky) yarn, 100g (3½oz), 70m (76yd) skeins

7(7:8) skeins in Sugared Almond

Hook and equipment

12mm (US O/17) crochet hook

Large tapestry needle

Size

To fit: S(M:L)

Finished measurements

Chest: 90(96:102)cm (35½(38:40½)in)

Length (nape to hem): 57(57:57)cm (22½(22½:22½)in)

Sleeve (underarm seam): 35(38:41)cm (13¾(15:16¼)in)

Tension

6 sts and 3.5 rows over 10cm (4in) using 12mm (US O/17) crochet hook

Abbreviations

See page 114

BODY

Ch32 loosely, join with a sl st to form a ring, being careful not to twist the chain. Make sure this loop fits over your head, it will loosen up!

Round 1: Ch4 (counts as 1 tr and 1 ch), 1tr into same space, 1tr into each of next 3 ch, (1tr, ch1, 1tr) in next ch, 1tr into each of next 11 tr, (1tr, ch1, 1tr) into next ch, 1tr into each of next 3 ch, (1tr, ch1, 1tr) into next ch, 1tr into each of next 11 tr, join rnd with a sl st to 3rd ch of ch 4, do not turn. (36 sts)

Note: The (1tr, ch1, 1tr) sets the points for the increases for the raglan sleeves. For orientation, the longer sections are the front/back and the shorter are the two sleeves.

Round 2: Sl st into ch 1 space, ch4 (counts as 1 tr and 1 ch), 1tr into same ch 1 space, *1tr into each of next 5 tr, (1tr, ch1, 1tr) into next ch 1 space, 1tr into each of next 13 sts,* (1tr, ch1, 1tr) into ch 1 space; rep from * to * once more, join rnd with a sl st into 3rd ch of ch 4. *(44 sts)*

Round 2 sets patt, with 1tr in each st and sleeve increases (1tr, ch1, 1tr) in every ch 1 space.

Work as set in rnd 2 until 8(9:10) rnds have been worked from foundation chain, join with a sl st to top of ch 3, do not fasten off yarn. *(92(100:108) sts)*

SHAPE ARMHOLES

I have increased here to give the sweater a boxy feel, this has been done by adding 4 sts, one either side of each armhole. Fold sweater along the 'side seams' so you can clearly see the front and back and armholes.

Round 9(10:11): Sl st into 1 ch space, miss 19 tr and 1 ch space and sl st in tr on other side of armhole (you have now joined the 2 sides), ch3 (counts as 1 tr), 1tr into same st, 1tr into each st to next armhole, work 2tr into st before armhole, miss the two 1 ch spaces and 19(21:23) sts, 2tr into next st to make 2nd armhole (to secure this armhole tie a scrap of yarn through the bottom of the 2 tr either side of armhole; don't worry about the rather large hole in each underarm, you can

seam this once you have finished the sweater), 1tr into each st to end of rnd, working last tr into top of ch 3 from previous rnd, join with a sl st to top of ch 3.

Round 10(11:12): Ch3 (counts as 1tr), 1tr into next st and into every st to end of rnd, working 2 tr into last st of rnd, join with a sl st to top of ch 3. *(58(62:66) sts)*

Rep rnd 10(11:12) without increasing in last st until sweater is required length; I have worked a total of 19 rounds from the foundation chain for the smallest size.

Final round: Ch1, 1dc into same space, 1dc into next st and into every st to end of rnd, join with a sl st to first dc, fasten off.

SLEEVES

(Make 2)

Round 1: Turn sweater upside down, join yarn to 2nd tr that remained unworked (from the (1tr, ch1, 1tr)), ch3 (counts as 1 tr) work 1tr into each of next 18(20:22) sts, join with a sl st to top of ch 3 (last tr should be on the unworked st of the other (1tr, ch1, 1tr)). *(19(21:23) sts)*

Round 2: Ch3 (counts as 1tr), 1tr into next st and into every st to end of rnd, join with a sl st to top of ch 3. *(19(21:23) sts)*

Rounds 3–5: Rep rnd 2.

Round 6 (decrease): Ch3 (counts as 1tr), tr2tog, 1tr into next st and every st to end of rnd, join with a sl st to top of ch 3. *(18(20:22) sts)*

Round 7: Rep rnd 2.

Round 8 (decrease): Rep rnd 6. *(17(19:21) sts)*

Round 9: Rep rnd 2.

Round 10 (decrease): Rep rnd 6. *(16(18:20) sts)*

Round 11: Rep rnd 2.

At this stage try on sweater and if needed cont working rnds 6 and 2 until sleeves are required length.

Last round: Ch1, 1dc into same space, 1dc into next st and into every st to end of rnd, join with a sl st to first dc, fasten off.

NECK EDGING

Join yarn to the centre back, ch1, 1dc into same space, work 1dc into each st to end of rnd, join with a sl st to top of first dc, fasten off. (You can, if you prefer, work another rnd of dc to make a slightly higher neckline.)

TO MAKE UP

Weave in ends (see page 125).

Sweater structure

You start from the neck and work down, increasing at the points where a raglan sleeve seam would be. Once you reach the point where the arms would start, you leave the sleeve stitches and carry on with just the body to the end of the sweater. Then it's just a case of finishing the sleeves off and you have a new wardrobe favourite!

CHAPTER 2
Scarves and Wraps

Whether you need something light and lacy for a summer evening party, or a warm and woolly number to snuggle into on a winter day, crochet is your best friend when it comes to making perfect scarves and wraps. And if you are a beginner to crochet, then start here, and don't be put off by the lace patterns; they are easier to work than you might think.

METALLIC *Luxury Cowl*

I think this is one of my favourite designs. The contrast of the squidgy Plump yarn and the fine metallic yarn creates a really beautiful effect, and it just oozes luxury! This is one of those designs that looks so tricky when in fact it just involves double crochet and chains and is easily a beginner project. You alternate the yarns – and crochet hooks – with each row and always work your trebles into spaces; it's so simple but so effective. And if you can't find a metallic yarn, choose something really silky (such as Blue Sky Fibers Alpaca Silk) instead and go for a more subtle contrast that will still look amazing!

Yarn

Mrs Moon Plump (80% superfine merino wool, 20% baby alpaca) super-chunky (super-bulky) yarn, 100g (3½oz), 70m (76yd) skeins
   3 skeins in Fondant Fancy (A)

Lanas Stop Platino (100% nylon) double knitting (light-worsted-weight) yarn, 50g (1¾oz), 200m (218yd) balls
   1 ball in Gold (B)

Hooks and equipment

10mm (US N/15) and 4mm (US F/5 or G/6) crochet hooks
Large tapestry needle

Size

60in (152cm) diameter and 9½in (24cm) deep

Tension

7 tr sts and 3 rows over 10cm (4in) using A and 10mm (US N/15) crochet hook

Abbreviations

See page 114

COWL

Using A and 10mm (US N/15) hook, make a chain of 111, join with a sl st to form a ring, being careful not to twist the chain. You need to have a multiple of 3 sts for the next row, which 111 is, but I have not allowed for an extra st when I join the chain as I find it leaves a bit of a gap because I have quite a loose tension. However, you may want to add an extra ch if you find the joined chain stitches too tight to work in to.

Round 1: Ch3 (counts as 1 tr), 1tr into next ch, and into every ch to end of rnd, join with a sl st to top of ch 3, fasten off.

Round 2: Using B and 4mm (US F/5 or G/6) hook, join yarn into space between any two tr, ch3 (counts as 1 tr), work 2tr into same space, *ch5, miss 3 tr, work 3tr into space between tr; rep from * to end of rnd, join with a sl st to top of ch 3, fasten off yarn and weave in ends.

Round 3: Using A and 10mm (US N/15) hook, join yarn into any ch 5 space, ch3 (counts as 1 tr), 2tr into same ch 5 space, 3 tr into next ch 5 space, and into every space to end of rnd. Join with a sl st to top of ch 3.

Rep rnds 2–3, weaving in ends of B as you go, until 7 rnds of A have been completed.

Next round: Using A and 10mm (US N/15) hook, ch1, 1dc into same st, and then into every st to end of rnd, join with a sl st to top of first dc, fasten off.

TO MAKE UP

Weave in ends of A (see page 125).

Weave as you go
Take the time to weave in the ends of the metallic yarn after each round. It's so slippery that it can unravel otherwise, and that is a tad annoying!

MANLY HOUNDSTOOTH *Scarf*

If you are looking for a really very simple project, here it is! Using only basic stitches, you can make this super-quick but totally lovely scarf, which is rather manly when worked in these colours, but you can obviously go to town with colour combinations! As I do with all luxury yarns, I've tried to make sure that there is very little wastage from your two skeins. To ensure that you have enough yarn, leave only very short tails – just long enough to weave in – when you switch colours.

Yarn

Blue Sky Fibers Worsted Hand Dyes (50% royal alpaca, 50% merino wool) Aran (worsted-weight) yarn, 100g (3½oz), 91m (100yd) skeins
  1 skein in Charcoal 2025 (A)
  1 skein in Midnight Blue 2013 (B)

Hook and equipment

6.5mm (US K/10½) crochet hook
Large tapestry needle

Size

156 x 11cm (61 ½ x 4½in)

Tension

9.5 sts and 9 rows over 10cm (4in) using 6.5mm (US K/10½) crochet hook, measured over dc/tr stitch pattern

Abbreviations

See page 114

SCARF

Using A, ch150 loosely. (The stitch pattern works with any multiple of 2, so it is easy to make the scarf longer or shorter – remember to purchase extra yarn if necessary.)

Row 1: 1dc into 4th ch from hook, *1tr into next ch, 1dc into foll ch; rep from * to end of row, finishing with 1dc, fasten off A, turn.

Row 2: Join in B, ch3 (counts as 1tr), miss st at base of ch 3, *1dc into next st, 1tr into foll st; rep from * to end of row (you should be working dc sts into tr sts and tr sts into dc sts), finish with 1dc into top of tch, fasten off B, turn.

Rep row 2, alternating between A and B. I worked 10 rows, finishing with a B row.

TO MAKE UP

Weave in ends (see page 125).

Starting the scarf

The scarf is worked lengthways, so you need to be very careful when you make your foundation chain that it is really loose. If it's too tight, not only will the first row be a nightmare, but the scarf will also curve to one side. If you have a problem creating an even, loose chain, use a crochet hook a few sizes larger for this, then switch back to a 6.5mm (US K/10½) hook for the first row.

RIPPLE *Shawl*

This gorgeous bit of fluff and sparkle is perfect for the sophisticated woman that I like to think I could be if life had taken a different path! It is the kind of shawl that is timeless and can be pulled out again and again when you need something to cover your shoulders over some strappy evening gown. The pattern is a basic ripple stitch, but uses two really special yarns; the contrast between the shiny metallic and the sumptuous fluffiness makes the effect really gorgeous. There is a chart as well as the written pattern to help you work the stitch.

Yarn

Mrs Moon Fluff (80% kid mohair, 20% silk) lace-weight (fingering) yarn, 25g (¾oz), 200m (218yd) skeins
  2 balls in Pavlova (A)

Rowan Anchor Artiste Metallic (80% viscose, 20% polyester) lace-weight (fingering) yarn, 25g (¾oz), 100m (109yd) balls
  2 balls in Gold 300 (B)

Hook and equipment

4mm (US F/5 or G/6) crochet hook
Large tapestry needle

Size

33 x 114cm (13 x 45in)

Tension

1.5 pattern reps and 9 rows over 10cm (4in) using 4mm (US F/5 or G/6) crochet hook

Abbreviations

See page 114

SHAWL

Using A, ch213 loosely.

Row 1: 2tr into 4th ch from hook, *1tr into each of foll 3 ch, [tr3tog] twice (so worked over next 6 ch, this is the decrease at the bottom of the wave), 1tr into each of next 3 ch, 3tr into each of next 2 ch (this is the increase at the top of the wave); rep from * to end of row, finishing after final decrease with 1tr into each of next 3 ch and 3tr into final ch, turn.

Row 2: Ch3 (counts as 1 tr), 2tr into st at base of ch3, *1tr into each of foll 3 sts, [tr3tog] twice (this should fall directly above the decrease on the row below), 1tr into each of next 3 sts, 3tr into each of foll 2 sts; rep from * to end of row, finishing with 1tr into each of last 3 sts, 3tr into top of tch (the missed sts at beg of row 1), turn, fasten off A.

Row 3: Join in B, ch3 (counts as 1 tr), 2tr into st at base of ch 3, *1tr into each of next 3 sts, [tr3tog] twice, 1tr into each of foll 3 sts, 3tr into each of foll 2 sts; rep from * to end of row, finishing with 1tr into each of last 3 sts and 3tr into top of tch, turn, fasten off B.

Rep row 3, working 3 rows of A followed by 1 row of B until 7 stripes of B have been worked in total, then work 2 rows of A, do not fasten off A.

Using the Fluff yarn

It can be a bit tricky working with the Fluff, just in terms of being certain of where the stitches are, so you might want to practise the stitch pattern with a smoother yarn first, just so you know what it's supposed to look like before you add in the Fluff complication!

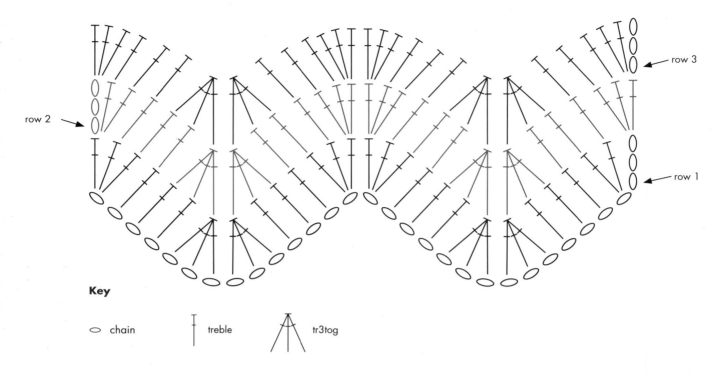

row 2 →

← row 3

← row 1

Key

⬭ chain	⊤ treble	⩒ tr3tog

EDGING

Cont in A, work 1 row of dc neatly down LH edge of shawl (as a general rule work 2dc along the length of each tr), fasten off yarn. Rep along RH edge.

Join B at top of LH edge, ch1, 1dc into same st, 1dc into each of next 2 sts, *ch3, sl st into 3rd ch from hook (picot made), miss next st, 1 dc into each of foll 3 sts; rep from * to bottom of edge, fasten off. Rep along RH edge.

TO MAKE UP

Weave in ends (see page 125).

Using the metallic yarn

Weave in the ends of the metallic yarn as you go as it is very slippery, and securing it straight away will avoid any unravelling disasters.

WATERFALL *Scarf*

This beautiful scarf looks complicated to make, but actually is quite simple once you have set the pattern up. It is a four-row repeat that becomes very clear early on, so it is easy to see if you have made a mistake, and there are constant reference points to ensure that you don't go astray! The gorgeous tones of blues are reminiscent of gushing water, but don't let that put you off choosing different shades: rich yellows and oranges would be amazing, or how about four tones of green? The scarf is joined in the middle so that the pattern cascades down to the ends on both sides; this means that you don't have a flat edge at one end and a pretty edge at the other!

Yarn

Blue Sky Fibers Alpaca Silk (50% alpaca, 50% silk) double knitting (sport-weight) yarn, 50g (1¾oz), 133m (146yd) skeins

2 skeins in Sapphire 137 (A)
1 skein in Plume 103 (B)
2 skeins in Oyster 115 (C)

Hook and equipment

3.5mm (US E/4) crochet hook
Large tapestry needle

Size

150 x 28cm (59 x 11in)

Tension

Each shell measures 7cm (2¾in) by 5cm (2in) using 3.5mm (US E/4) crochet hook

Abbreviations

See page 114

FIRST HALF OF SCARF

Using A, ch58.

Row 1: Work 1dc into 2nd ch from hook and into every ch to end of row, turn. *(57 sts)*

Row 2: Ch6, miss st at base of ch 6 and next dc, 1dc into next dc, *ch5, miss 2 dc, 1dc into next dc, ch5, miss 3 dc, 1dc into next dc, ch5, miss 2 dc, 1dc into next dc, ch5, miss 3 dc, 1dc into next dc; rep from * twice more, then rep again to last 2 sts, ch2, miss 1dc, 1tr into last dc, turn. *(17 loops)*

Row 3: Ch1, 1dc into first tr, ch5, 1dc into first ch 5 space, 7tr into next ch 5 space, *1dc into next ch 5 space, ch5, 1 dc into next ch 5 space, ch5, 1dc into next ch 5 space, 7tr into next ch 5 space; rep from * and after 4th set of 7tr groups finish with 1dc into next ch 5 space, ch5, 1dc into last ch 6 space, turn, fasten off.

Row 4: Join in B, ch5, 1dc into first ch 5 space, *1tr into next tr, (ch1, 1tr) into each of next 6 tr, 1 dc into next ch 5 space, ch5, 1dc into next ch 5 space; rep from * and after 4th set of tr groups finish with 1dc into next ch 5 space, ch2, 1tr into dc, turn, fasten off.

Row 5: Join in C, ch1, 1dc into tr, *(htr3tog, ch3, sl st into top of htr to make picot, ch2) into each of next 7 tr (do not work the final ch 2), 1dc into next ch 5 space; rep from * and after 4th set of tr groups finish with 1dc into last ch 5 space, turn, fasten off.

Row 6: Join in A, ch6, miss 2 picots, * 1 dc into ch 2 space (between picots 2 and 3), ch5, miss 1 picot, 1dc into next ch 2 space, ch5, 1dc into next ch 2 space, ch5, 1dc into next ch 2 space, ch5, miss 4 picots (2 picots from group you are working on and first 2 picots from next group); rep from * up to and including last 2 picots, ch2, 1dtr into last dc, turn. Rep rows 3–6, 14 times more.

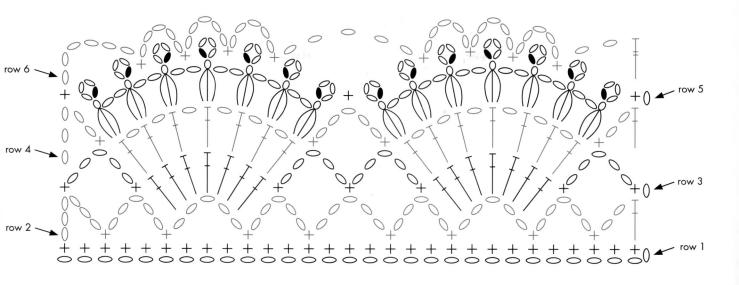

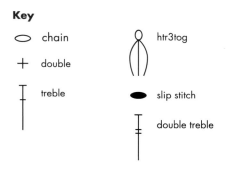

row 6

row 5

row 4

row 3

row 2

row 1

Key

○ chain

+ double

| treble

⬯ htr3tog

⬮ slip stitch

⫯ double treble

SECOND HALF OF SCARF

So that the pattern works down towards both ends of the scarf you need to work the second half from what will be the middle of the scarf (currently the base chain of the first side).

Turn the scarf to the wrong side (the cast-on tail should be at the opposite end to where you are about to start working) and work along the base chain as for patt row 2. Cont in patt as for first half until 15 reps are completed.

TO MAKE UP

Weave in ends (see page 125).

LARGE BOBBLE *Cross Treble Scarf*

I love everything about this scarf: the tassels that balloon like mini pompoms, the colour, the size, and the altogether bold statement that it makes! What's not to love? Crossing trebles is one of those techniques that looks very complicated and fancy, and in fact is so simple that you feel a little as though you're cheating by working it so easily. The stitch gives what could be quite a plain pattern a beautiful twist (quite literally), and is shown off to fabulous effect here. The quirky bobble fringe gives a great finish to the scarf, but is added on at the end, so if you'd rather leave it off, then that's no problem.

Yarn

Mrs Moon Plump (80% superfine merino wool, 20% baby alpaca) super-chunky (super-bulky) yarn, 100g (3½oz), 70m (76yd) skeins

7 skeins in Marmalade

Hook and equipment

10mm (US N/15) crochet hook

Large tapestry needle

Size

177 x 30cm (70 x 12in) (excluding tassels)

Tension

4 x cross trebles and 5 rows (2 cross treble rows and 3 dc rows) over 10cm (4in) using 10mm (US N/15) crochet hook

Abbreviations

ctr : cross treble = miss 1 st/ch, work 1tr, then work 1 tr into st/ch that was missed, going back across first tr made.

See also page 114

SCARF

Ch28 loosely.

Row 1 (ctr row): Work 1tr into 5th ch from hook, then 1tr into 4th ch from hook, crossing back across first tr made (first ctr made), miss next ch and work 1tr into next ch, then work back across last tr into ch that was missed (second ctr made); cont working ctr to last ch, 1tr into last ch, turn. *(12 ctr)*

Row 2 (dc row): Ch1 (does not count as st), 1dc into same st, 1dc into next st and into every st to end of row, working last dc into top of ch 3, turn. *(26 dc)*

Row 3 (ctr row): Ch3 (counts as 1tr), miss st at base of ch 3, *work 1ctr over foll 2 sts; rep from * to end of row, finishing with 1tr into last st, turn. *(12 ctr)*

Rep rows 2–3 until you have used up 6 skeins of yarn. Weigh the final skein, then work the bobble fringe on the starting end of the scarf, then weigh the skein again. The amount used is what is needed for the bobble fringe at the other end of the scarf, so wind off that amount. Then use the remainder of the skein to cont working rows 2–3, finishing with a row 2. Work bobble fringe along finishing end of scarf.

BOBBLE FRINGE

Attach yarn to a corner of starting edge, *ch8, tr3tog into 4th ch from hook, ch4, tr3tog into 4th ch from hook, sandwich the two groups together, and work a sl st through bottom of first tr3tog to secure (first bobble made), ch4, sl st into next 4 sts along on edge of scarf; rep from * along bottom edge of scarf. Do not worry too much if the spacing is not exactly even, but make sure the last bobble is made at the far corner: I made 7 bobbles at each end of the scarf.

TO MAKE UP

Weave in ends (see page 125).

OMBRÉ *Tassel Scarf*

This scarf is a very simple pattern made so beautiful by the stunning yarn. The yarn is from an independent dyer and runs from grey to pink on one giant ball. Independent dyers tend to use luxurious fibres and produce unique skeins of yarn using their own dying techniques. Choose any graduated 4ply (sock-weight) yarn and you will get a similar effect – the beauty of this is that no scarf will be the same as any other.

Yarn

Natali Stewart Gradient Seacell/Silk yarn (35% seacell, 65% silk) 4ply (sock-weight) yarn, 160g (5½oz), 640m (700yd) ball

1 ball in Red & Black

Hook and equipment

2.5mm (US B/1 or C/2) crochet hook
Tapestry needle

Size

128 x 29cm (50½ x 11½in) (excluding tassels)

Tension

7 groups of 3 tr (including 6 x 1 ch spaces) and 2 complete pattern reps over 10cm (4in) using 2.5mm (US B/1 or C/2) crochet hook

Abbreviations

See page 114

SCARF

Ch79 loosely.

Row 1: 1tr into 4th ch from hook, 1 tr into each of next 2 ch, *ch1, miss 1 ch, 1tr into each of next 3 ch; rep from * to end of row, finishing last 5 chs with ch1, miss 1 ch, 1tr into each of last 4 chs, turn.

Row 2: Ch3 (counts as 1tr), miss st at base of ch 3, 1tr into next st, *ch1, miss 1 st, 1tr into next st, 1tr into ch 1 space, 1tr into foll st; rep from * to last 3 sts, ch1, miss 1 st, 1tr into last st, 1tr into top of ch 3, turn.

Row 3: Ch3 (counts as 1tr), miss st at base of ch 3, *1tr into next st, 1tr into ch 1 space, 1tr into foll st, ch1, miss 1 tr; rep from * to last 4 sts, finishing with 1tr into next tr, 1tr into ch 1 space, 1tr into last st and 1tr into top of ch 3, turn.

Row 4: Ch1 (does not count as st), 1dc into first tr, ch5, miss 3 tr, 1dc into ch 1 space, *ch5, miss 3 tr, 1dc into next ch 1 space; rep from * to end of row, finishing with 1dc into last ch 1 space, ch5, miss 3 tr, 1dc into top of ch 3, turn.

Row 5: Ch5, 1dc into first ch 5 space, *ch5, 1dc into next ch 5 space; rep from * to end of row, finishing with 1dc into last ch 5 space, ch2, 1tr into dc, turn.

Row 6: Ch1 (does not count as st), 1dc into first tr, ch3, 1dc into first ch 5 space, *ch3, 1dc into next ch 5 space; rep from * to end of row, finishing with 1dc into last ch 5 space, turn.

Row 7: Ch3 (counts as 1tr), 3tr into first ch 3 space, *ch1, 3tr into next ch 3 space; rep from * to end of row, finishing with 3tr into last ch 3 space, 1tr into dc, turn.

Rep rows 2–7 until scarf measures desired length, finishing with a row 3.

TO MAKE UP

Weave in ends (see page 125).
Space 17 tassels evenly along each end of the scarf, attaching them with a standard cow hitch knot (see page 124).

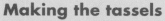

Making the tassels

If you want the tassels to match the colour of the yarn at each end of the scarf, then wind off yarn for first set before you start, and the final set when you get towards the end of the ball. I have put the tassels at contrasting ends, but you can make yours harmonious with the crochet if you prefer. I have made 17 tassels for each end, using 75cm (30in) per tassel, that's 25.5m (28¼yd) in total.

CHAPTER 3

For the Home

Crochet is the perfect craft for making gorgeous items for your home. Large, flat items – such as blankets, throws and rugs – show off the texture of crochet stitches beautifully, and allow for a lot of colour work without making the finished result look too busy. And using a chunky yarn and large hook will make even the biggest project grow more quickly than you might think.

BIG *Bedrunner*

This bedrunner is such a beautiful piece of crochet, and very easy to make. The possibilities of size and colour are endless and you can really have fun creating something completely original for your own room. The pattern is just a mix of doubles and trebles so it really is suitable for a total beginner. Also, using such a chunky yarn means that it grows very quickly, which is never a bad thing in my book!

Yarn

Mrs Moon Plump (80% superfine merino wool, 20% baby alpaca) super-chunky (super-bulky) yarn, 100g (3½oz), 70m (76yd) skeins

- 2 skeins in Pavlova (A)
- 2 skeins in Fondant Fancy (B)
- 2 skeins in Pistachio Ice Cream (C)
- 2 skeins in Peppermint Cream (D)
- 2 skeins in Gooseberry Fool (E)
- 2 skeins in Sugared Almond (F)

Hook and equipment

10mm (US N/15) crochet hook
Large tapestry needle

Size

147 x 58cm (58 x 22¾in)

Tension

6.5 sts and 6.5 rows over 10cm (4in) using 10mm (US N/15) crochet hook

Abbreviations

See page 114

BEDSPREAD

Using A, ch98.

Row 1: 1dc into 4th ch from hook, *1tr into next ch, 1dc into foll ch; rep from * to end of row, finishing with 1dc into last ch, turn, fasten off.

Row 2: Ch3 (counts as 1 tr), *1dc into next st, 1tr into foll st; rep from * to end of row, finishing with 1dc into top of tch, turn, fasten off.

Rep row 2, noting that you should be alternating dc and tr on each row, and every dc should work onto a tr from the row below, and changing colour as folls:

Row 3: B.
Row 4: C.
Row 5: D.
Row 6: E.
Row 7: F.
Row 8: F.
Row 9: E.
Row 10: D.
Row 11: C.
Row 12: B.
Row 13: A.
Row 14: A.

Rep rows 3–14 stripe patt twice more.

TO MAKE UP

Weave in ends (see page 125), or see below.

Changing the size

If you want to make the bedrunner larger or smaller, the pattern repeat is simply a multiple of two, and the length of the chain will be the final width. You can weave in the ends, but for this runner I have left them as a fringe; it's not just laziness, it looks great!

Working the foundation chain

One tip that will make a big difference is to make the foundation chain very loose. This is always a good idea in crochet, but particularly here if you are a total beginner; this is the one thing that could spoil the finish. If you find it difficult to create a loose chain, go up a hook size for this first bit, switching back to a 10mm (US N/15) hook for the first row.

THREE *Scatter Cushions*

These scatter cushions are a great place to start if you are new to crochet. They are great projects for trying out different types of granny square and practising doubles and trebles. The fun borders are all easy to create, too, and give the cushions a really lovely finish. The yarn specified is enough for all three cushions, but you can obviously just make one if you prefer. If you have a bigger cushion pad, why not make one of the granny square cushion covers and just keep going round and round, or making extra squares, until it fits! The patterns are just for the front of the cushions; I find it's better to back them with fabric. This helps them keep their shape and it also seems such a waste to crochet something that no one will ever see! You could however, mix and match these patterns for fronts and backs, which will mean you can get a change of look in your room with a flip of a cushion!

Yarn

Spud & Chloe Sweater (55% superwash wool, 45% organic cotton) Aran (worsted-weight) yarn, 100g (3½oz), 146m (160yd) skeins

3 skeins in Ice Cream 7500 (A)
1 skein in Watermelon 7512 (B)
1 skein in Pollen 7508 (C)
1 skein in Firefly 7505 (D)

Hook and equipment

4.5mm (US G/6 or H/8) crochet hook
Large tapestry needle
3 x 40cm (16in) square cushion pads or cushions with covers

Size

40cm (16in) square (excluding borders)

Tension

13 tr sts and 6.5 rows over 10cm (4in) using 4.5mm (US G/6 or H/8) crochet hook

Abbreviations

See page 114

FLOWER CUSHION

Using C, ch6, join with a sl st to form a ring.

Round 1: Ch6 (counts a 1tr and ch3), *1tr into ring, ch3; rep from * 6 more times, join with sl st to 3rd ch of ch 6, fasten off C. *(8 spokes and 8 spaces)*

Round 2: Join A to any ch 3 space, (1dc, ch2, 3tr, ch2, 1dc) into same space, *(1dc, ch2, 3tr, ch2, 1dc) into next ch 3 space; rep from * 6 times and do not join rnd at the end. *(8 sets of petals)*

Round 3: *Ch5, now work behind the petals from the previous row, miss 1 petal, 1dc into next tr of previous rnd (rnd 1, in between the petals); rep from * to end of rnd, do not join rnd at the end. *(8 x ch 5 loops)*

Round 4: *(1dc, ch2, 5tr, ch2, 1dc) into next ch 5 loop; rep from * to end of rnd, do not join rnd at the end. *(8 petals)*

Round 5: *Ch7, now work behind the petals from the previous row, 1dc into next dc of previous rnd (rnd 3); rep from * to end of rnd, do not join rnd at the end. *(8 x ch 7 loops)*

Round 6: *(1dc, ch2, 7tr, ch2, 1dc) into next ch 7 loop; rep from * to end of rnd, join with sl st to first dc, fasten off A. *(Flower is complete)*

The 'granny square' part of the cushion cover is worked directly onto the flower from rnd 7 onwards.

Round 7: Join B to any dc on rnd 5, working behind the petals, ch 3 (counts as 1tr), 2tr into same space, ch1, *(3tr, ch2, 3tr) into next dc of rnd 5 to make a corner, ch1, **3tr into next dc, ch1; rep from * twice then from * to ** only once more, join with a sl st to top of ch 3. *(4 corners and 4 sides)*.

Round 8: Sl st into next 2 tr and into ch 1 space, ch3 (counts as 1tr), 2tr into same space, ch1, *(3tr, ch2, 3tr) into corner space, ch1, 3tr into next space, ch1, 3tr into next space, ch1; rep from * to end of rnd, join with a sl st to top of ch 3.

Cont working as set in rnd 8 for 10 more rnds, working 3tr into

every ch1 side space, working 1ch in between each 3tr, and (3tr, ch2, 3tr) into every corner space. Work rnds 9 and 10 in B, rnds 11 and 15 in A, rnds 12, 13 and 14 in D, and rnds 16, 17 and 18 in C.

When joining a new colour, always join in a ch 1 space starting as folls: ch3 (counts as 1tr), 2tr into same ch space.

Round 19: Join A to any side st from rnd 19, ch1, 1 dc into same st, 1dc into every st and 1dc into every ch 1 space, working 2dc into every ch 2 corner space, join rnd with a sl st to top of first dc, do not fasten off yarn.

BOBBLE EDGING

Round 20: *Ch5, work htr3tog into 3rd ch from hook, secure yarn by yrh, ch2, htr3tog into 3rd ch from hook (top of previous htr3tog), sandwich the two groups together and secure with a sl st through the bottom of first group to form a bobble, ch3, miss 3 dc along the edge of

the cushion, join to edge with a sl st in foll st; rep from * around edge of cushion cover, missing just 1 st rather than 3 sts at each corner, join rnd with a sl st, fasten off.

STRIPY CUSHION

Using D, ch50.

Row 1: 1 dc into 4th ch from hook, *1tr into next ch, 1dc into foll ch; rep from * to end of chain, finishing with 1dc into last ch, fasten off D.

Row 2: Join in B, ch3 (counts as 1tr), miss st at base of ch 3, *1dc into next st, 1tr into foll st; rep from * to end of row, finishing with 1dc into top of ch 3, fasten off B.

Row 3: Join A; rep row 2.

Rep row 2 for a further 41 rows, changing colour on each row in order as set: D, B, A.

JOINING SQUARES

Lay the squares out flat in the order that you want them, or follow the photograph. Join squares to make horizontal strips, then join those to complete the cushion. With wrong sides facing and using A, work sl sts through both loops of each square. If you prefer you can sew the squares together, but I find it much easier to crochet them and the ridge between each square is a nice feature.

BORDER

Round 1: Join A to any ch 2 corner space, 3dc into same space, 1dc into every st and 1dc into every ch 1 space around cushion, working 3dc into every corner space. It is a bit tricky working over the seams; I have worked 1dc into each of the ch 2 spaces either side of a seam, but the main thing is to try and keep the sts as even as possible, join with a sl st to first dc made, do not fasten off.

Round 2: Ch3 (counts as 1tr), work 3tr into next st (corner turned), 1tr into next st, and into every st around cushion, working 3tr into every corner st (middle dc of 3 dc), join rnd with a sl st to top of ch 3, do not fasten off.

Round 3 (picot round): Ch1, 1dc into same st, *ch3, sl st into 3rd ch from hook, miss next st, 1dc into each of next 3 sts; rep from * around cushion, join with a sl st to first dc made, fasten off. Don't worry if the patt rep does not fit exactly!

BORDER

Round 1: Join A to any st along top of cushion, ch1, 1dc into same space, 1dc into every st evenly around cushion, working 3dc into every corner space. *(approx. 48 sts along each side, don't worry if it is not exact)*

Round 2: Ch3 (counts as 1tr), 1tr into next st, ch1, miss 1 st, *1tr into each of next 2 sts, ch1, miss 1 st; rep from *around edge, join with a sl st to top of ch 3, fasten off A.

Round 3: Join B to any ch 1 space in rnd 2, ch1, (1dc, ch3, 2tr), in same space and in every ch 1 space around edge, join with a sl st to first dc, fasten off.

MINI GRANNY SQUARES CUSHION

Make 25 squares in total; 9 with B centres, 8 with C centres and 8 with D centres.

Using a centre colour, ch6, join with a sl st to form a ring.

Round 1: Ch3 (counts as 1tr), 2tr into ring, ch1, *3tr into ring, ch1; rep from * twice more, join rnd with a sl st to top of ch 3, fasten off and weave in ends.

Round 2: Join A to any ch 1 space, ch3 (counts as 1tr), (2tr, ch2, 3tr) into same space as ch 3, ch1, *(3tr, ch1, 3tr), into next space, ch1; rep from * twice more, join rnd with a sl st to top of ch 3, fasten off and weave in ends.

TO MAKE UP

Weave in ends (see page 125).

If you are a skilled sewist then you can make up your own fabric cushion covers, but it's easy to simply sew the crochet panels to ready-made cushion covers. I found it simplest to do this by hand with the covers still on the pads. I pinned the crochet panel in place, making sure the decorative border extended beyond the edges of the cushions, then from the back and using matching sewing thread, I slip-stitched the panel to the cover along the cover seam lines.

COLOURFUL TWINE *Doormat*

This wonderful project is very much inspired by one of our loyal customers, Tina, who had created something similar for her camping trips. One thing that is immensely useful in a tent full of kids is a doormat to encourage everyone to realise that this might be a good place to take off their shoes! Being keen campers ourselves, it seemed sensible to give it a go, and it fits in perfectly at home, as well. There are many types and colours of twine, which is perfect for sturdy, hardwearing crochet – although I'm not sure I'd want to wear it! This is a super-simple design, just granny stripes with a border, but looks really lovely, and you can easily knock up another if it gets too grubby!

Yarn

Nutscene Heritage Jute Twine, 110m (120yd) spools

2 spools in Natural (A)
1 spool in Pink (B)
1 spool in Saffron (C)
1 spool in Lilac (D)
1 spool in Dove (E)

Note that 4 or 5 spools in total would be enough if using fewer colours

Hook and equipment

5.5mm (US I/9) crochet hook
Large tapestry needle

Size

81 x 53cm (32 x 20¾in)

Tension

3 groups of 3 trebles and 4.5 rows over 10cm (4in) using 5.5mm (US I/9) crochet hook

Abbreviations

See page 114

DOORMAT

Using A, ch92 (stitch patt is a multiple of 4).
Row 1: 2tr into 4th ch from hook, ch1, miss 3 ch, *3tr into next ch, ch1, miss 3 ch; rep from * to end of row, working 3tr into last ch, fasten off, turn. *(23 groups of 3tr)*
Row 2: Join in B, ch4 (counts as 1 tr, ch1), 3tr into first ch 1 space, * ch1, 3tr into next ch 1 space; rep from * to end of row, finishing with 1 group of 3tr into last ch 1 space, ch1, 1tr into top of ch 3, fasten off, turn. *(22 groups of 3tr)*
Row 3: Join in A, ch3 (counts as 1 tr), 2tr into the first ch 1 space, * ch1, 3tr into next ch 1 space; rep from * to end of row, finishing with 3tr into last ch 4 space, fasten off, turn. *(23 groups of 3tr)*
Rep rows 2–3 until 25 rows have been worked in total, or as many rows as required, alternating colours in the foll sequence: A, B, A, C, A, D, A, E, beginning with a C row and finishing with an A row, do not fasten off.

BORDER

Round 1: Ch1, 1dc into same place, 1dc into next st and into every st around the mat, working 3dc into each corner, join rnd with a sl st into first dc made, fasten off.
Round 2: Join in C, ch1, 1dc into same place, 1dc into each of next 2 sts, *ch3, sl st into 3rd ch, miss 1 st, 1dc into each of next 3 sts; rep from * to end of rnd, fasten off.

TO MAKE UP

Weave in ends (see page 125).

HOT WATER BOTTLE *Cover*

When you are feeling low, or cold or maybe a bit of both, what could be better than cuddling up with a hot water bottle enclosed in a super-soft, super-gorgeous, hand-crocheted cover? I'm feeling better already! This is a lovely use of three muted colours, but you can have as much fun as you want with your own choices. The tiny squares have been crocheted together, which gives a really neat finish and also gives a lovely ridge around each square. You can have the ridge on the inside if you prefer, it makes no difference to the finished product.

Yarn

Mrs Moon Plump DK (80% superfine merino wool, 20% baby alpaca) double knitting (light-worsted-weight) yarn, 50g (1¾oz), 115m (125yd) skeins

2 skeins in Pavlova (A)
1 skein in Earl Grey (B)
1 skein in Gooseberry Fool (C)

Hook and equipment

4.5mm (US G/6 or H/8) crochet hook
Large tapestry needle

Size

21cm (8¼in) wide and 28cm (11in) high (unstretched) to fit a standard hot water bottle

Tension

Each granny square measures 7cm (2¾in) square

Abbreviations

See page 114

SQUARE

SQUARE A
Make 13 squares as folls: Round 1: B. Round 2: C. Round 3: A.

SQUARE B
Make 16 squares as folls: Round 1: C. Round 2: B. Round 3: A.

Using first colour, ch6, join with a sl st to form a ring.
Round 1: Ch3 (counts as 1 tr), 2tr into ring, *ch2, 3tr into ring; rep from * twice more, finishing with ch2, join with a sl st to top of first ch 3, fasten off.
Round 2: Join second colour to any ch 2 space, ch3 (counts as 1 tr), (2tr, ch2, 3tr) into same ch 2 space, ch1, *(3tr, ch2, 3tr) into foll ch 2 space, ch1; rep from * twice more, after final ch1 join rnd with a sl st to top of ch 3, fasten off.
Round 3: Join A to any ch 2 space, ch3 (counts as 1 tr), (2tr, ch2, 3tr) into same ch 2 space, *ch1, 3tr into next ch 1 space, ch1, (3tr, ch2, 3tr) into next ch 2 space; rep twice more from * to final corner, 3tr into final ch 1 space, ch1, join with a sl st to top of ch 3, fasten off A.

TO MAKE UP
Weave in ends (see page 125).
You can sew the squares together, though I have crocheted them together by slip stitching. I find this method quicker and easier, as I am rubbish at sewing; and it is easy to pull back if you go wrong.
To make the front, arrange 15 C-centre squares in five rows of three squares (see diagram, right). With wrong sides together (so that the slip stitch ridge is on the right side), join all the horizontal rows to form long strips, slip stitching into the back

loop only of each square. Then join the long strips to form the rectangle. Attach the remaining C-centre square to top of the central square, as shown.

To make the back, arrange 12 B-centre squares in four rows of three squares. Join them as for the front and then attach the remaining square to the top.

Place both sides wrong sides together, carefully matching up the stitches. Starting at the LH side of the top, join the pieces by working 1dc into each stitch, going through both loops of the stitch on each piece. Work dc2tog into the inner corner and 4dc into the outer corner down the LH side. Leave the bottom flap open. Rejoin yarn on RH side and work as for the LH side.

You can leave the flap as it is and tuck it in once the hot water bottle is inside, but if you prefer you can sew two buttons on the outside of the shorter back side of the cover. Position the buttons so that you can fasten them into existing spaces in the granny squares.

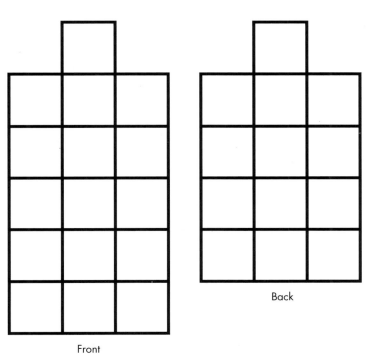

Front

Back

FLOWER *Blanket*

The sublime colours of the Sweet Georgia yarn in this blanket give it a fabulously retro, yet timeless feel. It is the kind of throw that you can imagine being on a sofa for years, cuddling generations and remaining a constant in changing lives. The clever stitch pattern creates flowers that interlock. The petals of each flower are easily created by trebling two stitches together so although the pattern looks rather complicated, it is in fact very easy to get the hang of and the chart shows you how the flowers link together.

You can of course make this blanket as large as you like: if you want to practise first, why not make a small cushion cover or even a scarf? As always, have fun with colours – find a yarn that you love and go wild!

Yarn

Sweet Georgia Superwash DK (100% superwash merino wool) double-knitting (light-worsted-weight) yarn, 115g (4oz), 234m (256yd) skeins

3 skeins in Birch (A)
1(2) skein(s) in Saffron (B) (see border note in patt)
1 skein in Bison (C)
1 skein in Dutch (D)

Hook and equipment

4mm (US F/5 or G/6) crochet hook
Large tapestry needle

Size

Approx. 86 x 100cm (34 x 39in)

Tension

2 flowers plus 2 sts and 7 rows over 10cm (4in) using 4mm (US F/5 or G/6) crochet hook

Abbreviations

See page 114

BLANKET

Using A, ch 201 loosely. (Stitch patt is a multiple of 11 + 3.)

Row 1 (RS): 1dc into 2nd ch from hook, ch1, miss 1 ch, 1dc into next ch, [ch3, miss 3 ch, 1dc into next ch] twice, *ch2, miss 2 ch, 1dc into next ch, [ch3, miss 3 ch, 1dc into next ch] twice; rep from * to last 2 ch, ch1, miss 1 ch, work 1dc into last ch, turn.

Row 2: Ch3, (tr2tog, ch2, tr2tog) into first ch 1 space, ch1, miss 1dc and ch 3 space, 1dc into next dc, *ch1, miss ch 3 space, [tr2tog, ch2] 3 times into next ch 2 space then tr2tog (still into same ch 2 space), ch1, miss 1dc and ch 3 space, 1dc into next dc; rep from * to last 2 sets of spaces, ch1, miss ch 3 space, (tr2tog, ch2, tr2tog) in ch 1 space, tr into last dc, fasten off A, turn.

Row 3: Join in B, ch1, 1dc into first dc, *ch3, 1tr2tog into top of each of next 4 tr2tog, ch3, 1dc into ch 2 space (this should be ch 2 space in middle space of 4 tr2tog from row 2); rep from * to end, working last dc into top of ch 3.

Row 4: Ch1, 1dc into first dc, *ch3, 1dc into top of first tr2tog, ch2, miss 2 tr2tog, 1dc into top of next tr2tog, ch3, 1dc into next dc; rep from * to end, finishing with 1dc into last dc, turn.

Row 5: Ch1, 1dc into first dc, *ch1, miss ch 3 space, [tr2tog, ch2] 3 times into next ch 2 space, then tr2tog (still into same ch 2 space), ch1, miss ch 3 space, 1dc into next dc; rep from * to end of row, finishing with 1dc into last dc, fasten off B, turn.

Row 6: Join in A, ch3, tr2tog into each of next 2 tr2tog, ch3, 1dc into next ch 2 space (that is the space between the 2nd and 3rd tr2tog of row 5), ch3, *tr2tog into next 4 tr2tog, ch3, 1dc into next ch 2 space, ch3; rep * to end of row, finishing with tr2tog into each of last 2 tr2tog, 1tr into last dc, turn.

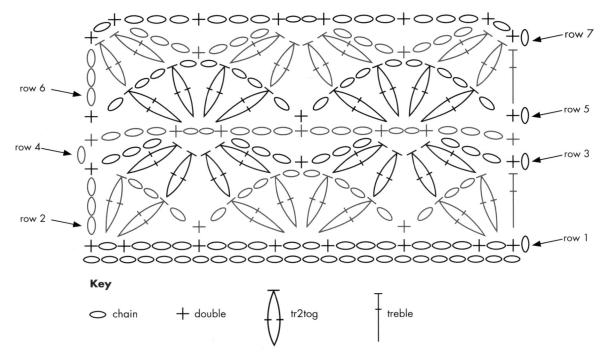

Key

○ chain   + double   ◇ tr2tog   ⊤ treble

Row 7: Ch1, 1dc into first tr, ch1, miss 1 tr2tog, 1dc into next tr2tog, ch3, 1dc into next dc, ch3, *1dc into next tr2tog, ch2, miss 2 tr2tog, 1dc into next tr2tog, ch3, 1dc into next dc, ch3; rep from * to last 2 tr2tog, work 1 dc into first of these, ch1, 1dc into top of ch3, turn.

Rep rows 2–7, changing to C on row 9, then back to A for foll 3 rows, then to D for next 3 rows. Cont in stitch patt as set, alternating the colours B, C, D every 3 rows with 3 rows of A in between each of those colours until 6 D stripes have been worked. Work 1 more row in A.

BORDER

The border is worked in B, though only a little of a second skein is needed for the pattern as written, so you could make a much more substantial border if you wish. If you prefer no border, then a second skein of B is not needed.

Round 1: Join yarn to top RH corner, ch1, 1dc into same space, work 1 rnd of dc evenly around edge of blanket, working 3dc into same stitch in every corner. Finish rnd by joining with a sl st to top of first dc.

Round 2 (picot round): *Ch3, dc into 3rd ch from hook (1 picot made), miss next st, sl st into foll st to secure picot to edge, sl st into next 2 sts; rep from * around blanket, fasten off.

TO MAKE UP

Weave in ends (see page 125).

TEXTURED *Cushion*

Crochet is great for creating texture. All sorts of bumps and bobbles can be made really easily, and they produce beautiful effects on the simplest of items. This giant cushion is a case in point. The simple bobbles are made by crocheting four trebles together. It's very easy once you've done it once, and the bobbles are really effective. I've used two muted tones in stripes that accentuate the differences in texture, but keep the cushion looking stylish. You could go for a brighter, more contrasting stripe for a jazzier cushion, according to taste!

Yarn

Rowan Cocoon (80% merino wool, 20% kid mohair) chunky (bulky) yarn, 100g (3½oz), 115m (126yd) balls
3 balls in Scree 803 (A)
4 balls in Alpine 802 (B)

Other materials

60cm (23½in) square cushion pad

Hook and equipment

7mm (US K/10½) crochet hook
Large tapestry needle

Size

60cm (23½in) square

Tension

9 sts and 7 rows over houndstooth patt over 10cm (4in) using 7mm (US K/10½) crochet hook

Abbreviations

MB = make bobble by working tr4tog into same space.
See also page 114

CUSHION FRONT

Using A, ch51. (Stitch patt is a multiple of 4 + 3.)
Row 1(RS): 1tr into 4th ch from hook, 1tr into next ch and into every ch to end of row, fasten off, turn.
Row 2: Join in B, ch1 (does not count as st), 1dc into each of the first 2 sts, *MB in next st, 1dc into each of next 3 sts; rep from * to last 3 sts, MB in next st, 1 dc into next st, 1dc into top of ch 3, fasten off, turn.
Row 3: Join in A, ch3 (counts as 1 tr), miss st at base of ch 3, 1tr into next st, *1dc into top of bobble, 1tr into each of next 3 sts; rep from * to end of row, finishing with 1dc in top of last bobble, 1tr into each of last 2 sts, fasten off, turn.
Row 4: Join in B, ch1, 1dc into same place, 1dc into each of next 3 sts, *MB in next st , 1dc into each of next 3 sts; rep from * to end of row, 1dc in top of ch 3, fasten off, turn.
Row 5: Join in A, ch3 (counts as 1 tr), miss st at base of ch 3, *1tr into each of next 3 sts, 1dc into top of bobble; rep from * to end of row, finishing with 1tr into each of last 4 sts.
Rep rows 2–5 until work measures 60cm (23½in) or the size of the cushion pad, finishing with either a row 3 or 5. I am a loose crocheter and have worked 20 bobble rows but you should have plenty of yarn if you need to do more rows.
Next row (fold row): Join in B, ch1, 1 dc into same place, 1dc into next st and into every st to end of row, turn.

You should be working dc onto the tr from the row below and tr onto the dc from the row below; this alternating of stitches gives the houndstooth effect.

If you are doing a different-size cushion and the base number of stitches is even, then every row starts with a tr (that is, ch3) and finishes with a dc.

TO MAKE UP

Weave in ends (see page 125).

Right side in, fold the cushion in half along the fold row. Work a row of sl st along the edge just worked and then evenly down one side (as a general rule work one stitch in the side of a dc and two into the side of a tr). Turn the cushion right side out, insert the cushion pad and then, using A, sew up the final edge.

CUSHION BACK

Next row: Join in A, ch3 (counts as 1 tr), miss st at base of ch 3, *1dc into next st, 1tr into next st, rep from * to end of row, finishing with 1tr into last st, fasten off, turn.

Next row: Join in B, ch1, 1dc into same place, *1tr into next st, 1dc into foll st; rep from * to end of row, finishing with 1dc into last st, turn.

Rep last 2 rows until back matches front in length, finishing with an A row, do not fasten off.

Making up the cushion

I've given a contrast pattern for the back of the cushion, but you could easily back it with fabric if you prefer.

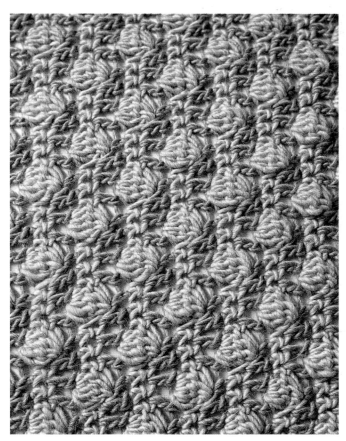

SUPER *Rug*

Super-simple, super-fabulous and super-quick! This is a great, giant project that you can finish in a couple of hours. The very thick yarn grows incredibly quickly and is great fun to work with. Despite its size, this is just a very simple pattern, which could equally be a placemat if you used a 4ply yarn! After creating a basic circle of trebles, the fun border is added in a contrast colour to give the whole thing real zing. Enjoy!

Yarn

Bernat Mega Bulky (100% acrylic) super-chunky (super-bulky) yarn, 300g (11¼oz), 58m (63yd) balls
  2 balls in Light Grey Heather 88046 (A)
  3 balls Radiant Orchid 88314 (B)

Hook and equipment

20mm (US S/35) crochet hook
Large tapestry needle

Size

90cm (35¾in) diameter

Tension

4.5 tr sts and 2 tr rows over 10cm (4in) using 20mm (US S/35) crochet hook

Abbreviations

MP = make picot. A picot is made by ch3 and then slip stitching into the 3rd ch from hook.
See page 114

CENTRE OF RUG

Using A, ch8, join with a sl st to form a ring, being careful not to twist the chain.
Round 1: Ch3 (counts as 1 tr), work 14 tr into ring, join rnd with a sl st to top of ch 3. *(15 tr)*
Round 2: Ch3 (counts as 1 tr), 1tr into same place, 2tr into next st and into every st to end of rnd, join rnd with a sl st to top of ch 3. *(30 tr)*

Round 3: Ch3 (counts as 1 tr), 1tr into same place, 1tr into next st, *2tr into next st, 1 tr into next st; rep from * to end of rnd, join rnd with a sl st to top of ch 3. *(45 tr)*
Round 4: Ch3 (counts as 1 tr), 1tr into same place, 1tr into each of next 2 sts, *2tr into foll st, 1tr into each of next 2 sts; rep from * to end of rnd, join with a sl st to top of ch 3. *(60 tr)*
Round 5: Ch3 (counts as 1 tr), 1tr into same place, 1tr into each of next 3 sts, *2tr into foll st, 1tr into each of next 3 sts; rep from * to end of rnd, join with a sl st to top of ch 3. *(75 sts)*
Round 6: Ch3 (counts as 1 tr), 1tr into same place, 1tr into each of next 4 sts, *2tr into foll st, 1tr into each of next 4 sts; rep from * to end of rnd, join with a sl st to top of ch 3. *(90 tr)*
Fasten off A.

PINK EDGING

Round 1: Join in B, ch1 (does not count as st), 1dc into same place, *ch3, miss 2 sts, 1dc into next st, ch1, miss 1 st, 1dc into next st; rep from * to end of rnd, finishing with ch1, miss last st, join with a sl st to the first dc made.
Round 2: Sl st twice into first ch 3 space (to get to the right place to start this rnd), ch3 (counts as 1 tr), 3tr into ch 3 space, *1tr into next ch 1 space, 4tr into next ch 3 space; rep from * to end of rnd, finish with 1tr into last ch 1 space, join with sl st to top of ch 3.
Round 3: Sl st in next st (to get to the right place to start this rnd), ch1 (does not count as st), 1dc into same st, *ch1, miss next tr, 1dc into foll tr, ch3, miss 2 tr, 1dc into next tr; rep from * finishing with ch 3, join with a sl st to first dc made.
Round 4: Sl st into next ch 1 space, ch6, sl st into 3rd ch from hook (1tr and picot made), * (1tr, ch1, 1tr (MP), ch1, 1tr (MP), ch1, 1tr) in foll ch 3 space, (1tr (MP)) into foll ch 1 space; rep from * to end of rnd, finishing after a ch 3 space, join with sl st to 3rd ch of ch 6.

TO MAKE UP

Weave in ends (see page 125); you will probably need to do this with your fingers!

CAMPING *Throw*

This is the ultimate easy-to-make crochet project – a fabulous, brightly coloured, enormous granny square, finished with a great fun border. It is a perfect blanket and you will have it for years and years, be it as a picnic blanket, a baby blanket, a throw for the sofa, a bedspread or an essential camping companion, which is what I use this one as! I've used a hard-wearing merino yarn that you don't need to worry about being used and abused – it can take it!

Yarn

Rico Essentials Soft Merino Aran (100% merino superwash) Aran (worsted-weight) yarn, 50g (1¾oz), 100m (109yd) balls

    4 balls in Sun Yellow 67 (A)
    4 balls in Coral 78 (B)
    4 balls in Melon 06 (C)
    2 balls in Red 08 (D1)
    2 balls in Brick Red 07 (D2)
    4 balls in Candy 16 (E)
    2 balls in Cream 61 (F1)
    2 balls in Natural 60 (F2)

Hook and equipment

4.5mm (US G/6 or H/8) crochet hook
Large tapestry needle

Size

123 x 123cm (48½ x 48½in)

Tension

5 groups of 3tr and 4 ch2 spaces, and 8 rows over 10cm (4in) using 4.5mm (US G/6 or H/8) crochet hook

Abbreviations

See page 114

BLANKET

Using A, ch6, join with a sl st to form a ring.
Round 1: Ch3 (counts as 1 tr), 2tr into ring, *ch2, 3tr into ring; rep from * twice more finishing with a ch2, join with a sl st to top of first ch 3, fasten off.
Round 2: Join B to any ch 2 space, ch3 (counts as 1 tr), (2tr, ch2, 3tr) into same ch 2 space, ch1, *(3tr, ch2, 3tr) into foll ch 2 space work, ch1; rep from * twice more, after final ch1 join rnd with a sl st to top of ch 3, fasten off.
Round 3: Join C to any ch 2 space, ch3 (counts as 1 tr), (2tr, ch2, 3tr) into same ch 2 space, *ch1, 3tr into next ch 1 space, ch1, (3tr, ch2, 3tr) into next ch 2 space; rep from * twice more to final corner, work 3tr into final ch 1 space, ch1, join with a sl st to top of ch 3, fasten off.
Round 4: Join D1 to any ch 2 space, ch3 (counts as 1 tr), (2tr, ch2, 3tr) into same ch 2 space, *(ch1, 3tr) into next two ch 1 spaces, ch1, (3tr, ch2, 3tr) into next ch 2 space; rep from * twice

Choosing yarns

Granny square blankets are traditionally made up of leftover scraps of yarn – hence their garishness – and I have given a nod to that tradition here. I bought a few colours first and when I went back to buy more, I could no longer get hold of a couple of shades, so you will see that there are two reds and a cream and a white. I wanted to show that precise colours really don't matter; the blanket looks absolutely amazing and a little bit of imperfection makes it all the more perfect!

more, after final corner space, (ch1, 3tr) into each of final two ch 1 spaces, ch1, join the round with a sl st to top of ch 3.

Round 5 and beyond: Rep row 4 using E. As the blanket grows, there will be more ch 1 side spaces and cont working 3tr into each of these, separated by a ch1. In each of the four corner spaces work (3tr, ch2, 3tr). Change colour every round in the sequence A, B, C, D, E, switching from D1 to D2 when necessary.

BORDER

Round 1: Join F1 to any ch 2 corner space, work one ordinary granny square row, as above, do not fasten off, do not turn.

Round 2: Ch1, 1dc into same place, 1dc into each of next 2 sts, into ch 2 space work (2dc, ch2, 2dc), cont working a dc round by working 1dc into each tr, 1dc into each ch 1 space and into each ch 2 corner space work (2dc, ch2, 2dc), finishing rnd by joining with a sl st to top of first dc, do not turn.

Round 3: Ch1, 1dc into same place, 1dc into each of next 4 sts, into ch 2 corner space work (2dc, ch2, 2dc), cont around, working 1dc into every st and (2dc, ch2, 2dc) into each corner space, join rnd with a sl st to top of first dc, fasten off yarn, do not turn.

Round 4 (picot fan): Join F2 to any ch 2 corner space, ch6 (counts as 1 tr, ch 3), [1tr, ch3] 3 more times into same ch 2 corner space, 1tr into same ch 2 corner space to finish fan, miss 2 sts, 1dc into foll st, *miss 3 sts, (1tr, ch3) into foll st 5 times, finish with 1tr into same st, miss 3 sts, 1dc into foll st; rep from * around blanket.

You should be working the last fan before every corner in about the 6th st before the ch 2 corner space: work the fan in this st, miss 3 sts, 1dc into next st, miss 1 st then work the corner fan, after the corner fan miss 1 st, 1dc into foll st and then rep from * to next corner. However, do not worry if this is not exactly the case! If the fan is worked in the 8th st before the corner, just make sure you miss 3 sts and make 1 dc into next st. If after this you have more or fewer than 1 st before the corner space, it will not show in the finished blanket. Finish rnd with last dc before corner, sl st into 3rd ch of ch 6, fasten off yarn.

TO MAKE UP

Weave in ends (see page 125).
Press the blanket.

No colour change

If you do not want to change colour every round, you need to sl st into each of next 3tr and into the ch 2 space, then work as instructed. You must move to next space along as every round starts in a space.

CHAPTER 4

Accessories

The small size of accessory projects means that they are pleasingly quick to make, even if you are using finer yarn than for blankets or sweaters. And you can easily crochet with materials other than conventional yarn; the very practical – yet still good-looking – shopping bag in this chapter is made from jute twine!

PUFF *Mitts*

There are times when crochet needs to look a little less like crochet – needs to lose that laciness and make a fabric that is a bit more knit-like. Mittens are a case in point; to fulfil their basic role as handwarmers, they need a bit more structure than crochet normally gives.

I hope that these mittens have solved that problem. They are a bit more tricky than a lot of the projects in this book, but once you are familiar with the stitch pattern it isn't actually difficult, so practice with some spare yarn before starting the project. I'd really recommend giving the mitts a go; they are so lovely when finished!

Yarn

Mrs Moon Plump DK (80% superfine merino wool, 20% baby alpaca) double knitting (light-worsted-weight) yarn, 50g (1¾oz), 115m (125yd) skeins

1 skein in Gooseberry Fool

Hook and equipment

4mm (US F/5 or G/6) crochet hook
Large tapestry needle

Size

20cm (8in) long (including trim) and 9cm (3½in) wide (unstretched)

Tension

15 dc sts and 12 dc rows over 10cm (4in) using 4mm (US F/5 or G/6) crochet hook
15 htr sts and 12 htr rnds over 10cm (4in) using 4mm (US F/5 or G/6) crochet hook

Abbreviations

See page 114

LEFT-HAND MITTEN

CUFF

Ch11 loosely.
Row 1: Work 1dc into 2nd ch from hook, 1dc in every ch to end, turn. *(10 sts)*
Row 2: Ch1 (does not count as st), 1dc in BLO of same space, work 1dc BLO into next st and into each st to end of row, turn. *(10 sts)*
Rep row 2 until 28 rows in total have been worked, do not fasten off.
Place the two ends together and join seam by working a sl st through each st across first and last rows to form a tube, do not fasten off. This is the cuff finished!
Turn the cuff anti-clockwise 90 degrees.

HAND

Round 1: Ch1, 1dc into same space, work 1dc into end of each row around cuff (28 sts in total), join rnd with a sl st into top of first dc made, do not turn, cont working in the round throughout.
Round 2: Ch2 (counts as 1 htr), work 1htr into next st and into every st to end of rnd, join rnd with a sl st to top of ch 2, do not turn. *(28 sts)*
Rep rnd 2 until 8 complete htr rnds have been worked. Try the mitt on now to see if it is long enough to start the thumbhole; if not work as many more rnds of htr as needed.**

MAKE THUMBHOLE

Round 9: Ch2 (counts as 1 htr), 1htr into next st, ch6, miss 5 sts, work 1htr into next st and into every st to end of rnd, join with a sl st to top of ch 2.
Round 10: Ch2 (counts as 1 htr), 1htr into next st, work 5htr into ch 6 space, 1htr into next st and into every st to end of rnd, join with a sl st to top of ch 2. *(28 sts)*
***Work three straight htr rnds (as for rnd 2). Try mitt on to see if it fits, and work more rnds if needed.
Round 14: Ch1 (does not count as st), 1dc into same space, work 1dc into next st and into each st to end of rnd, join rnd with a sl st to top of first dc. *(28sts)*

Mitten structure

You begin by making a crochet rib, which is a great technique to have mastered. The rib is worked sideways and then joined into a tube before starting the main body of the mitt. The mitts are both worked the same way other than the position of the thumb, which is placed on each mitt so that the 'seam' that appears as you move up rows is on the palm rather than the top of each mitt. Working into the back loop only (BLO) of each stitch creates a lovely, stretchy fabric. The shell trim and thumbs are optional. Consider using a contrast colour for the rib and shell edging, or make the rib extra-long for a more luxurious pair of mittens. Remember to purchase extra yarn if you plan on lengthening the mittens.

Round 15 (shell trim): Ch1 (does not count as st), sl st into same space, *miss one st, work 5 htr into next st, miss one st, sl st into next st; rep from * to end of rnd, working final sl st into first sl st made to join, fasten off and weave in ends. (7 shells)

MAKE THUMB

Join yarn to first htr (on RH side of hole), ch2 (counts as 1 htr) work 1htr into each of the 4 sts, then work 7 htr evenly around the other side of the thumbhole, join with a sl st to top of ch2. (12 sts)

If this looks like too many or too few stitches, just add or subtract sts evenly until there are as many as looks right.

Thumb row 2: Ch2 (counts as 1 htr), work 1htr into each st around, join with a sl st to top of ch 2.

Thumb row 3: Ch1, 1dc into same space, 1 dc into every st around, join with a sl st to first dc made, fasten off.

RIGHT-HAND MITTEN

Work as for left-hand mitten to **.

MAKE THUMBHOLE

Round 9: Ch2 (counts as 1 htr), 1htr into each of next 20 sts, ch6, miss 5 sts, 1htr in each of last 2 sts, join with a sl st to top of ch 2.

Round 10: Ch2 (counts as 1 htr), 1htr into each st to ch 6 space, work 5htr into ch 6 space, 1htr in each of last 2 sts, join with a sl st to top of ch 2. (28 sts)

Work as for left-hand mitten from *** to end.

TO MAKE UP

Weave in ends (see page 125).

PUFF BOBBLE *Beret*

This fun beret has a distinctly Celtic feel to it, but without the pompom and mix of colours it has a more Parisian vibe... it's up to you to decide which you prefer. This is a lovely small project and great if you've never done puffs before. They have real depth and give a completely different look to crochet, creating a fabric that looks as though it's been woven rather than crocheted. The beret is worked in the round, so there is no seaming to do afterwards. This also gives a beautiful look on the top of the beret where all the increases radiate out from the middle.

Yarn

Rooster Almerino Aran (50% baby alpaca, 50% merino wool) Aran (worsted-weight) yarn, 50g (1¾oz), 94m (102yd) balls
  2 balls in Rooster 310 (A)
  1 ball in Brighton Rock 307 (B)

Hooks and equipment

4.5mm (US G/6 or H/8) and 5mm (US H/8 or I/9) crochet hooks
Large tapestry needle

Size

One size: 20cm (8in) high (not including pompom), and 48cm (19¾in) circumference at rim (unstretched)

Tension

7 puffs and 8 rows over 10cm (4in) using 5mm (US H/8 or I/9) crochet hook

Abbreviations

PUFF = htr4tog in same space, yrh and pull through to secure. See also page 114

BERET

Using A, make a crochet magic ring.
Round 1: Using 5mm (US H/8 or I/9) hook, ch1, work 6dc into the ring, pull ring tight and join round with a sl st into top of 1st dc made.
Round 2: Ch2 (counts as 1 htr), htr3tog (this with the ch2 counts as first PUFF) into 1st dc, *ch1, PUFF into next dc; rep from * to end, after last PUFF do not ch1, but 1tr into top of first PUFF made to finish round (1tr acts as the last space between puffs and no sl st is required to join the round; working the tr here gets you neatly in the right place to start next rnd).
Round 3: Ch2 (counts as 1 htr), htr3tog in same space working around the tr of the previous row (this is the space between 6th and 1st PUFF of rnd 2), ch1, 1 PUFF into same space, *ch1, (1 PUFF, ch1, 1 PUFF) into next ch1 space (between PUFFs of previous rnd); rep from * to end of rnd, join with 1tr to top of 1st PUFF.

Round 4: Ch2 (counts as 1 htr), htr3tog around tr, ch1, (PUFF, ch1, PUFF) into next ch 1 space, *ch1, 1 PUFF into next ch 1 space, ch1, (PUFF, ch1, PUFF) into next ch 1 space; rep from * to end of rnd, join with 1tr to top of 1st PUFF.

Round 5: Ch2 (counts as 1 htr), htr3tog around tr, ch1, 1 PUFF into next ch 1 space, ch1, (PUFF, ch1, PUFF) into next ch 1 space, (this should be in the ch 1 in (PUFF, ch1, PUFF) from the previous rnd), *ch1, (1 PUFF, ch1) into each of next two ch 1 spaces, (PUFF, ch1, PUFF) into next ch 1 space; rep from * to end of rnd, join with 1tr to top of 1st PUFF.

Round 6: Ch2 (counts as 1 htr), htr3tog around tr, ch1, (1 PUFF, ch1) into each of next two ch 1 spaces, (PUFF, ch1, PUFF) into next space, *ch1, (1 PUFF, ch1) into each of next three ch 1 spaces, (PUFF, ch1, PUFF) into next space; rep from * to end of rnd, join with 1tr to top of 1st PUFF.

Round 7: Ch2 (counts as 1 htr), htr3tog around tr, ch1, (1 PUFF, ch1) into each of next three ch 1 spaces, (PUFF, ch1, PUFF) into next ch 1 space, *ch1, (1 PUFF, ch1) into each of next four ch 1 spaces, (PUFF, ch1, PUFF) into next space; rep from * to end of rnd, join with 1tr to top of 1st PUFF.

Round 8: Ch2 (counts as 1 htr), htr3tog around tr, ch1 (1 PUFF, ch1) into each of next four ch 1 spaces, (PUFF, ch1, PUFF) into next ch 1 space, *ch1, (PUFF, ch1) into each of next five ch 1 spaces, (PUFF, ch1, PUFF) into next ch 1 space; rep from * to end of rnd, join with 1tr to top of 1st PUFF.

Round 9: Ch2 (counts as 1 htr), htr3tog around tr, ch1, (PUFF, ch1) into each of next five spaces, (PUFF, ch1, PUFF) into next ch 1 space, *ch1, (PUFF, ch1) into each of next six spaces, (PUFF, ch1, PUFF) into next ch 1 space; rep from * to end of rnd, join with 1tr to top of 1st PUFF.

Round 10 (straight): Ch2 (counts as 1 htr), htr3tog around tr, (ch1, PUFF) into each ch 1 space to end of rnd, join with 1tr to top of 1st PUFF. *(48 PUFF)*

Rounds 11–12: Rep rnd 10.

Round 13 (smaller PUFF): Ch2, htr2tog around tr, (ch1, htr3tog) into each ch 1 space to end of rnd, join with 1tr to top of 1st PUFF, do not fasten off. *(48 PUFF)*

BAND

Round 1: Using 4.5mm (US G/6 or H/8) hook, ch1, 1dc around tr, 1dc into top of next PUFF, *1dc into next ch 1 space, 1dc into top of next PUFF; rep from * to end, join with a sl st to top of 1st dc, fasten off A. *(96 sts)*

Round 2: Join in B, ch1, 1dc into same place and 1dc into every st to end of rnd, join with a sl st to top of 1st dc, fasten off B.

Round 3 (decrease rnd): Join in A, ch1, 1dc into same place, *1dc into each of next 3 sts, dc2tog; rep from * to end of rnd, join with a sl st to top of 1st dc, fasten off A. *(77 sts)*

Rounds 4–8: Rep rnd 2, alternating colour on every row. If the hat is too tight, do not work as many rounds on the rim. If it is too loose, work another rnd 3.

TO MAKE UP

Weave in ends (see page 125).

POMPOM

Using both A and B together, make a pompom and attach it to the centre of the beret by threading the ends of yarn used to tie the pompom together through either side of the centre of the beret and tying them tightly in a double knot. This helps avoid pompom wobble, which is disconcerting for all involved!

TWINE *Shopping Bag*

Like the Colourful Twine Doormat (see page 58), this project makes perfect use of this wonderfully coloured, hard-wearing fibre! There are so many different colour combinations you could go for, but equally, a natural bag seems right, too. Ours is very patriotic in its glorious red, white and blue, but you could go for all sorts of colour combinations depending on your mood or nation! The bag has a solid base, so that unlike the string bags of the '70s you can actually put things in this one without fear of them dropping out straight away! I've gone for short handles, but you can easily lengthen these if you want an over-the-shoulder version.

Yarn

Nutscene Fabulous Blond Twine, 150m (164yd) in a can
  1 can of Blond (A)

Nutscene Heritage range 110m (120¼yd) spools
  1 spool in Lilac (B)

Note that you only require a small amount of this for the edging around the top of the base, and you can use A instead if you prefer.

Nutscene CandyTwist Twine, 100m (109yd) spools
  1 spool in Red, White & Blue (C)

Hook and equipment

4.5mm (US G/6 or H/8) crochet hook
Large tapestry needle

Size

35cm (13¾in) high and 28cm (11in) wide

Tension

10 tr sts and 5 tr rows over 10cm (4in) using 4.5mm (US G/6 or H/8) crochet hook

Abbreviations

See page 114

BAG

Using A, ch6, join with a sl st to form a ring, being careful not to twist the chain.

Round 1: Ch3 (counts as 1 tr), work 13tr into ring, join rnd with a sl st into top of ch 3, do not turn. *(14 sts)*

Round 2: Ch3 (counts as 1 tr), 1tr into same place, 2tr into next st and into every st to end of rnd, join rnd with sl st to top of ch 3. *(28 tr)*

Round 3: Ch3 (counts as 1 tr), 1tr into same place, 1tr into next st, *2tr into next st, 1tr into next st; rep from * to end of rnd, finishing with 1tr into last st, join with a sl st to top of ch 3. *(42 tr)*

Round 4: Ch3 (counts as 1 tr), 1tr into same place, 1 tr into each of next 2 sts, *2tr into next st, 1 tr into each of next 2 sts; rep from * to end of rnd, finishing with 1tr into each of last 2 sts, join with a sl st to top of ch 3. *(56 tr)*

Round 5: Ch3 (counts as 1 tr), 1tr into same place, 1 tr into each of next 3 sts, *2tr into next st, 1 tr into each of next 3 sts; rep from * to end of rnd, finishing with 1tr into each of last 3 sts, join with a sl st to top of ch 3. *(70 tr)*

Round 6: Ch3 (counts as 1 tr), 1tr into same place, 1 tr into each of next 4 sts, *2tr into next st, 1 tr into each of next 4 sts; rep from * to end of rnd, finishing with 1tr into each of last 3 sts, join with a sl st to top of ch 3. *(84 tr)*

Round 7: Ch3 (counts as 1 tr), 1tr into next st and into every st to end of rnd, join with a sl st to top of ch 3. *(84 tr)*

Round 8: Ch1, 1dc into same place, 1 dc into next st and into every st to end of rnd, join with a sl st to top of first dc, fasten off A.

Round 9: Join in B, ch1, 1dc into same place, 1 dc into next st and into every st to end of rnd, join with a sl st to top of first dc, fasten off B. Note that if you prefer, you can work this rnd in A.

Round 10: Join in C, ch1, 1dc into same place, *ch 5, miss 2dc, 1dc into next st, rep from * to last 2dc, miss 2dc, sl st to top of first dc.

Round 11: To get to the right place to start next rnd, sl st twice into next ch 5 space, ch1, 1dc into same ch 5 loop, *ch5, 1dc into next ch 5 loop; rep from * to end of rnd, ch5, sl st to top of first dc.

Rep rnd 11 until the bag is required length; this bag measured 35cm (14in) high with the netting slightly stretched. Fasten off B.

Rim round 1: Join A into any ch 5 space, ch3 (counts as 1 tr), 1tr into same sp, *1tr into next dc, 2tr into next space; rep from * around rim, join with a sl st to top of ch 3.

Rim round 2: Ch1, 1dc into same place, 1dc into next st and into every stitch to end of rnd, join with a sl st to top of first dc made, fasten off.

HANDLES

(Make two)
Using A, ch 50 (or length required).
Row 1: 1htr into 3rd ch from hook and into every ch to end of row, fasten off.

TO MAKE UP

Weave in ends (see page 125).
Sew handles in place using A.

SNOWBOARDER'S *Hat*

You obviously don't need to snowboard to wear this hat, or even ski – to be honest it doesn't even need to be worn somewhere snowy... What I mean to imply by the name is that this hat is super-cool! I'm sure any snowboarder would love to wear it. It's also super-easy to make. The hat is crocheted in the round starting at the top, so there is no sewing up to be done at the end and it's easy to make it bigger or smaller according to your needs.

Yarn

Cascade Pacific (60% acrylic, 40% superwash merino wool) Aran (worsted-weight) yarn, 100g (3½oz), 195m (213yd) skeins
   1 skein in Cream 01 (A)
   1 skein in Persimmon 84 (B)

Hook and equipment

7mm (US K/10½) crochet hook
Large tapestry needle

Size

56cm (22in) circumference (to fit an average adult head) and 21cm (8¼in) from top to bottom

Tension

9 htr and 8 rows over 10cm (4in) using 7mm (US K/10½) crochet hook

Abbreviations

See page 114

HAT

Using 2 strands (take one from the centre of the ball and one from the outside) of A, ch4, join with a sl st to form a ring.

Round 1: Ch2 (counts as 1 htr), work 9 htr into ring, join with a sl st to top of ch 2, do not turn. *(10 sts)*

Round 2: Ch2 (counts as 1 htr), 1htr into same st (at base of ch 2), 2htr into next st (this is quite difficult to see as it looks very close to the ch 2), 2htr into each st to end of rnd, join with a sl st to top of ch 2, do not turn. *(20 sts)*

Round 3: Ch2 (counts as 1 htr), 1htr into same st, 1htr into next st, *2htr into foll st, 1htr into next st; rep from * to end of rnd, finishing with 1htr in last st, join with a sl st to top of ch 2, do not turn. *(30 sts)*

Round 4: Ch2 (counts as 1 htr), 1htr into same st, *1htr into each of next 2 sts, 2htr into foll st; rep from * to end of rnd, finishing with 1htr into each of last 2 sts, join with a sl st to top of ch 2, do not turn. *(40 sts)*

Round 5: Ch2 (counts as 1 htr), 1htr into same place *1htr into each of next 3 sts, 2htr into foll st; rep from * to end of rnd, finishing with 1htr into each of last 3 sts, join with a sl st to top of ch 2, fasten off A, do not turn. *(50 sts)*

Break A and join in 2 strands of B, holding both strands together.

Round 6: Ch2 (counts as 1 htr), 1htr into foll st and into every st to end of rnd, join with a sl st to top of ch 2. *(50 sts)*

Rounds 7–15: Rep rnd 5. You can make the hat larger of smaller here, just keep trying it on for size. Work 5 rnds in total using B, then break 1 strand of B and join in 1 strand of A, holding A and B together. Work 5 rnds using A and B strands.

Round 16 (rim): Ch1, 1dc into same place, work 1dc into every st to end of rnd, join with a sl st to top of first dc made, fasten off yarn.

TO MAKE UP
Weave in ends (see page 125).

POMPOM
Make a pompom using both colours, keeping ends quite long after you have tied it and using these to attach the pompom to the hat.

PLAITS
(Make 2)
Cut 3 x 1m (1yd) lengths of both colours of yarn. Lay the 6 strands together, pick up in the middle and using a crochet hook pull through the rim and hitch to make a long tassel. Plait the yarn (you should have 12 strands, so divide into groups of 4, mixing the colours); when it is the desired length, tie a knot and trim ends. Repeat on opposite side of rim.

Choosing yarns
The hat is crocheted with two strands of yarn held together, using two different colours either on their own or mixed together. This gives such a great effect and adds a bit of fun to this lovely beanie.

PINWHEEL CLUTCH *Bag*

This clutch bag is a great way to show off crochet at its best! The interlocking circles produced by pinwheel stitch create a really eye-catching geometric pattern, particularly when using a stark contrast in colours as I have done here. Pinwheels are very simple to create: you work groups of trebles together in one place – easy to achieve for a new crocheter. Any strong cotton yarn would work, and you can make the bag bigger by adding extra pattern reps from the start. There is a chart as well as the written pattern to help you work the stitch.

Yarn

Rico Essentials Cotton DK (100% cotton) double-knitting (sport-weight) yarn, 50g (1¾oz), 130m (142yd) balls
1 ball in Royal 36 (A)
1 ball in White 80 (B)

Hooks and equipment

3mm (US C/2) crochet hook and 4.5mm (US G/6 or H/8) crochet hook (for the handle)
Large tapestry needle

Size

13 x 25cm (5 x 10in)

Tension

Each pinwheel measures 3 x 3cm (1¼ x 1¼in)

Abbreviations

See page 114

BAG

Using 3mm (US C/2) crochet hook and A, ch56 loosely.
Row 1: 1dc into 2nd ch from hook, 1dc into next ch, *miss 3 ch, 7tr into foll ch, miss 3 ch, 1dc into each of next 3 ch; rep from * to end of row, finishing last 4 ch with miss 3 ch, 4tr into last ch, fasten off A, turn.
Row 2: Using B, ch1, 1dc into same place, 1dc into next st, *ch3, tr7tog, ch3, 1 dc into each of next 3 sts; rep from * to end of row, finishing with tr4tog over last 4 sts, turn.
Row 3: Ch3 (counts as 1 tr), 3tr into same place, *miss ch 3, 1dc into each of foll 3 dc, miss ch 3, 7tr into top of tr7tog; rep from * to end of row, finishing with miss ch 3, 1dc into each of last 2 sts, fasten off B, turn.
Row 4: Using A, ch3 (counts as 1 tr), miss st at the base of ch 3, tr3tog over next 3 sts, *ch3, 1dc into each of next 3 sts, ch3, tr7tog; rep from * to end of row, finishing with ch3, 1dc into last tr, and 1dc into top of ch 3, turn.
Row 5: Ch1, 1dc into same place, 1dc into next st, *miss ch 3, 7tr into top of tr7tog, miss ch 3, 1dc into each of next 3 dc; rep from * to end of row, finishing with 1dc into each of last 3 dc, miss ch 3, 4tr into top of 3trtog, fasten off A, turn.
Rep rows 2–5 until 17½ complete pinwheels (35 rows) have been worked, or it measures approx. 35cm (14in). Finish with a row 3 or 5 to make a scalloped edge for the fold-over flap.

TO MAKE UP

This bag has been made up so the wrong side is on the outside, as I preferred the pattern that way. However, whatever you decide, weave in the ends on the inside (see page 125). Fold up the lower third of the crochet, matching up the pattern along the edge. Sew the side seams. I measured out a piece of stiff card to fit inside the bag and covered this with fabric to give the bag some structure. Lining the bag with some contrasting fabric would also look great.

HANDLE LOOP

Using 4.5mm (US G/6 or H/8) crochet hook and two strands of B held together, join the yarn to the top RH corner of the bag (under the flap) ch35, join ch to bag in same place with a sl st, fasten off and weave in ends.

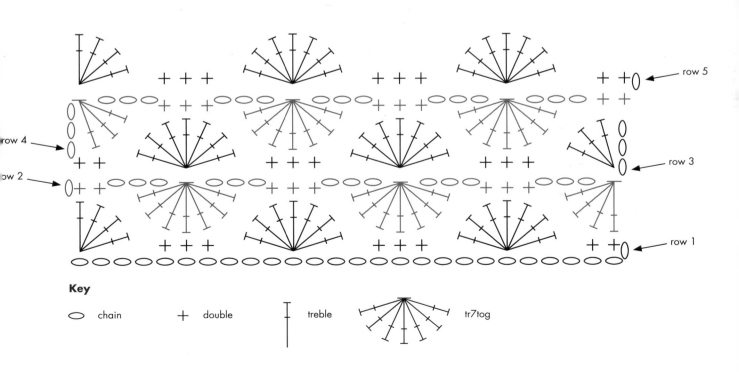

Key

⬭ chain   + double | treble   tr7tog

MEDALLION *Choker*

Intricate crochet stitches really lend themselves to jewellery; they can be works of art in themselves and sometimes just need a bit of extra showing off. This beautiful choker mixes a crochet cotton with a silver thread that makes it looks as though it is actually made of metal, but has the benefit of being soft enough to wear. The choker is a simple four-row pattern, so this is a great project for gifts! You can get many out of one ball of each yarn. The roundels are created by working groups of trebles into loops; really not difficult at all and very effective! I'm making loads for my friends' birthdays this year.

Yarn

Rico Essentials Crochet Cotton (100% cotton) lace weight (fingering) yarn, 50g (1¾oz), 260m (284yd) balls
1 ball in Steel Grey 19 (A)

Sajou Metallic Thread (100% polyester), 225m (246yd) spool
I spool in silver (B)

Hook and equipment

2.25mm (US B/1) crochet hook
Large tapestry needle

Size

53cm (21in) long (including ties)

Tension

Each roundel to measure approximately 2.5cm (1in) using 2.25mm (US B/1) crochet hook and one strand each of A and B held together

Abbreviations

See page 114

CHOKER

Use one strand each of A and B held together throughout. Ch112 loosely.

Row 1: 1dc into 2nd ch from hook, 1dc into every st to end of ch, turn.

Row 2: Sl st into first 25 sts, ch4 (counts as 1 tr, ch 1), miss st at base of ch 4 and next st, *1tr into foll st, ch1, miss next st; rep from * until only 25 sts remain unworked (not including st just missed), 1tr into next st, leave rem sts unworked, turn.

Row 3: Ch1, 1dc into first st, 1dc into next ch 1 space, *ch3, then a further ch7, sl st into 7th ch from hook, turn work (this makes it easier to work into the loop) and then (1dc, 1htr, 12tr, 1htr, 1dc) into 7ch loop, ch3, miss next (1tr, ch1, 1tr), work 1dc into next ch 1 space, [1dc into next tr and 1dc into foll ch 1 space] twice (5dc in total); rep from * to end, finishing after final (8th) roundel with ch3, 1dc into ch 4 space, 1dc into 3rd ch of ch 4, fasten off.

TO MAKE UP

Weave in ends (see page 125).
Press to make choker lie flat.

CHAPTER 5
For Children

Crochet does make it easy to embrace the super-cute factor when you're making projects for children or for the nursery. As well as cosy things to wear and blankets to snuggle up into, this chapter includes two of the most adorable toys, which are bound to become firm favourites for boys and girls alike.

CHILD'S *Cowl*

In my experience, scarves are just too tricky for kids; they either have them dragging along the ground or end up tangling themselves up. The whole point should be to keep them warm, and this cowl is just about perfect for that!

COWL

Using 2 strands (take one from the centre of the ball and one from the outside) of A, ch44 loosely. Check the chain fits round your child's head; if it doesn't seem long enough add two or four more stitches, though remember it will stretch a bit. Making sure the chain is not twisted, join it with a sl st to form a ring.

Round 1: Ch1 (does not count as st), 1dc into same place, 1dc into next st and into every st to end of rnd, join with a sl st to top of first dc, do not turn. *(44 sts)*

Change to one strand each of B and C, holding both strands together.

Round 2: Ch2 (counts as 1 htr), 1htr into next st and into every st to end of rnd, join with a sl st to top of ch 2, do not turn.

Rounds 3–14: Rep rnd 2.

Fasten off B and C, and join in 2 strands of A.

Round 15: Ch1, 1dc into same place, 1dc into next st and into every st to end of rnd, join with a sl st to top of ch 2, fasten off.

TO MAKE UP

Weave in ends (see page 125).

Yarn

Rooster Almerino Aran (50% merino wool, 50% baby alpaca) Aran (worsted-weight) yarn, 50g (1¾oz), 94m (103yd) balls
  Small amount of Smoothie 324 (A)
  1 ball in Custard 305 (B)
  1 ball in Silver 320 (C)

Hook and equipment

7mm (US K/10½) crochet hook
Large tapestry needle

Size

55cm (21¾in) circumference and 22cm (8¾in) deep

Tension

8 htr and 7 rows over 10cm (4in) using 7mm (US K/10½) crochet hook

Abbreviations

See page 114

CHILD'S *Beanie*

This lovely child's hat has a matching cowl (see page 92). It is a great, easy project suitable for a beginner, and creates a lovely gift very, very quickly! The beanie is exactly what you want from a child's hat – simple, fun, warm and easy to spot in a crowd! Both projects use the same yarn, which is two colours held together; this gives a lovely marl effect where the colours randomly twist around each other. You do not need to wind the two colours into one ball before using the yarn, simply hold one strand from each separate ball at the same time.

Yarn

Rooster Almerino Aran (50% merino wool, 50% baby alpaca) Aran (worsted-weight) yarn, 50g (1¾oz), 94m (103yd) balls

1 ball in Custard 305 (A)
1 ball in Silver 320 (B)
1 ball in Smoothie 324 (C)

Hook and equipment

7mm (US K/10½) crochet hook
Large tapestry needle

Size

50cm (20in) circumference and 19cm (7½in) from top to rim

Tension

8 htr and 7 rows over 10cm (4in) using 7mm (US K/10½) crochet hook

Abbreviations

See page 114

HAT

Using A and B together, ch4, join with a sl st to form a ring.

Round 1: Ch2 (counts as 1 htr), work 9htr into the ring, join with a sl st to top of ch 2, do not turn. *(10 sts)*

Round 2: Ch2 (counts as 1 htr), 1htr into same st (at base of ch 2), 2htr into next st (this is quite difficult to see as it looks very close to the ch 2), 2htr into each st to end of rnd, join with a sl st to top of ch 2, do not turn. *(20 sts)*

Round 3: Ch2 (counts as 1 htr), 1htr into same st, 1htr into next st, *2htr into foll st, 1htr into next st; rep from * to end of rnd, finishing with 1htr in last st, join with a sl st to top of ch 2, do not turn. *(30 sts)*

Round 4: Ch2 (counts as 1 htr) 1htr into same st, *1htr into each of next two sts, 2htr into foll st; rep from * to end of rnd, finishing with 1htr into each of last 2 sts, join with a sl st to top of ch 2, do not turn. *(40 sts)*

Round 5: Ch2 (counts as 1 htr), 1htr into foll st and into every st to end of rnd, join with a sl st to top of ch 2, do not turn. *(40 sts)*

Rounds 6–13: Rep rnd 5. You can make the hat larger or smaller here, just keep trying it on for size.

Fasten off A and B and join in 2 strands of C (take one from the centre of the ball and one from the outside) at the back of the hat.

Round 14 (trim): Ch1, 1dc into same place, 1 dc into every st to end of rnd, join with a sl st to first dc made, fasten off.

TO MAKE UP

Weave in ends (see page 125).

POMPOM

Make a fabulous pompom using C. Keep ends quite long after you have tied it and use these to attach the pompom to the hat.

Colours

If you do not want to do a contrast pompom and trim, you should have enough of the main colours to just use these instead.

DEEP CHEVRON *Baby blanket*

Ripples and chevrons are the mainstay of crochet and this lovely baby blanket is a great twist on a classic chevron. I should say that it is little more complicated than the standard chevron, so if you are a beginner to crochet it is probably worth learning the basic stitch first (see page 111). However, as with all crochet, once you've got started you should find it easy to keep going. There is a chart as well as written instructions to help you work this stitch pattern.

Yarn

Blue Sky Fibers Worsted Cotton (100% organic cotton) Aran (worsted-weight) yarn, 100g (3½oz), 137m (150yd) skeins

1 skein in Sleet 635 (A)
1 skein in Drift 614 (B)
1 skein in Shell 606 (C)
1 skein in Pink Parfait 642 (D)
1 skein in Lotus 617 (E)

Hook and equipment

4.5mm (US G/6 or H/8) crochet hook
Large tapestry needle

Size

80 x 67cm (31½ x 26¼in)

Tension

1 pattern rep (20 sts and 6 rows) over 10cm (4in) using 4.5mm (US G/6 or H/8) crochet hook

Abbreviations

Group = 1tr, ch1, 1tr worked into same space.
See also page 114

BLANKET

Using A, ch143 loosely. (The stitch patt is a multiple of 20 +3 if you want to make the blanket larger or smaller.)

Row 1: 1tr into 5th ch from hook, ch1, 1tr into same space, *ch1, miss 3 ch, (1tr, ch1, 1tr) into next ch, ch1, miss 3 ch, (1tr, ch1, 1tr, ch3, 1tr, ch1, 1tr) into next ch, ch1, miss 3 ch, (1tr, ch1, 1tr) into next ch, ch1, miss 3 ch, **(1tr, ch1, 1tr) into next ch, do not ch1, miss 3 ch, (1tr, ch1, 1tr) into next ch; rep from * to last 3 ch, you should be at ** in the patt, (1tr, ch1, 1tr) into 3rd ch from end, miss 1 ch, 1tr into last ch, turn.

Row 2: Ch3 (counts as 1 tr), miss first group from row 1, (1tr, ch1, 1tr) into first ch 1 space between last two groups of row 1, *ch1, miss next group, (1tr, ch1, 1tr) into next ch 1 space between groups, ch1, (1tr, ch1, 1tr, ch3, 1tr, ch1, 1tr) into ch 3 space, ch1, miss next group from row 1, work (1tr, ch1, 1tr) into next ch 1 space between groups, ch1, miss next group from row 1, work (1tr, ch1, 1tr) into next ch 1 space, **do not ch1, miss the decrease group from row 1, (1tr, ch1, 1tr) into next ch 1 space; rep from * to ch 1 space before final group, you should be ** in the patt, do not ch1, work 1tr into top of turning ch from row 1. Fasten off A, turn.

PATTERN REPEAT

Row 3 and every row thereafter is essentially a repeat of row 2, however, there are two main differences.

1: All stitches, apart from the increase group, are worked into the stitches 2 rows below (row 1 when working row 3). The increase group is worked as normal into the ch 3 space in the row below (row 2 when working row 3).

2: The (1tr, ch1, 1tr) groups are now worked into the ch 1 space within each group (from 2 rows below), NOT into the ch 1 space between groups.

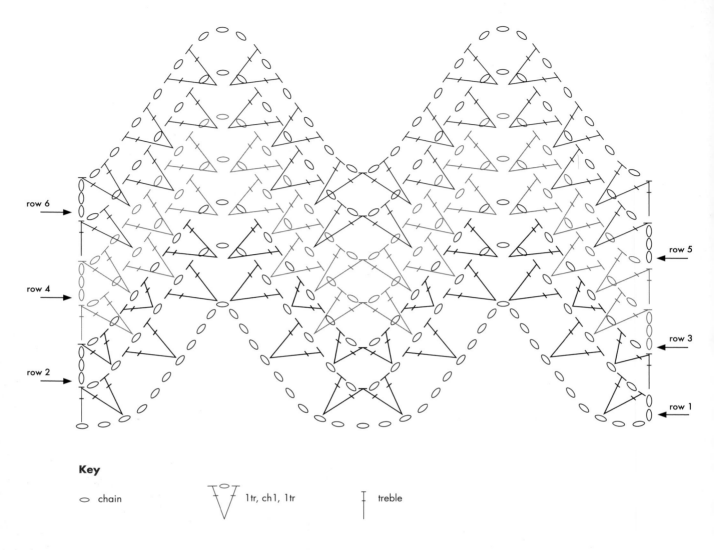

row 6
row 4
row 2
row 5
row 3
row 1

Key

○ chain

1tr, ch1, 1tr

treble

Make a rainbow

I've chosen a fairly muted palette, but you could go wild with the colours! If you don't know the sex of the baby then a rainbow is always fabulous, and the Blue Sky yarn colours are perfect for this. Working into two rows below means that the colours run into each other beautifully, so be brave!

Row 3: Join B, ch3 (counts as 1 tr), miss first group from row 1 and ch 1 space, work a group in ch 1 space within second group, *ch1, work another group into next group from row 1, ch1, (1tr, ch1, 1tr, ch3, 1tr, ch1, 1tr) into ch 3 space from row 2, ch1, work a group into next group from row 1, ch1, work a group into next group, **do not ch1, miss decrease group from row 1, work a group into foll group in row 1; rep from *, you should finish at ** in second-to-last group from row 1, do not ch1, miss final group, 1tr into top of ch 3, turn.

Rep row 3, changing colour every two rows until 40 rows have been worked in total. Then rep row 3, 5 times more and changing colour on every row to make a single-row striped band across the top of the blanket. Remember to work all stitches in the spaces from two rows below, apart for the increase; so for row 4 you are working into row 2, and so on.

TO MAKE UP

Weave in ends (see page 125).
Press blanket following instructions on ball band.

BABY *Cardigan*

There is something so special about crafting a cardigan for a new baby, not just because you are creating a unique item for a new life, but also because you can use luxury yarns to make your cardigan super-gorgeous. This cardi is based on a very traditional design: it starts at the top and gradually increases over the bobble yoke section before you split off the sleeves. There is nothing tricky at all about the pattern, so please do have a go even if you've never tried making a garment before.

Yarn

Blue Sky Fibers Baby Alpaca Melange (100% baby alpaca) double knitting (sport-weight) yarn, 50g (1¾oz), 100m (110yd) skeins

2 skeins in Toasted Almond 809 (A)
1 skein in Cotton Candy 810 (B)

Other materials

3 x buttons 1.5cm (⅝in) in diameter

Hook and equipment

3.75mm (US F/5) crochet hook
Large tapestry needle

Size

To fit: 3–6(6–9:9–12) months
Finished measurements
Chest: 42(52:60)cm (18½(20½:23¾in)
Length (nape to hem): 22(23:24)cm (8¾(9:9½)in)

Tension

18 tr sts and 9 tr rows over 10cm (4in) using 3.75mm (US F/5) crochet hook

Abbreviations

BOBBLE = htr3tog in same space, yrh and pull through to secure.
See also page 114

CARDIGAN

Cardigan is made from the top down in one piece.
Using A, ch46(50:56) loosely.
Row 1: Work 1dc into 2nd ch from hook and into every ch to end, turn. *(45(49:55) sts)*
Row 2: Ch1, 1dc into same place, 1dc into every st to end, fasten off A, turn.
Row 3: Join in B, ch3 (counts as 1 htr, ch 1), miss st at the base of ch 2 and foll st, *BOBBLE into next st, ch1, miss next st; rep from * to end of row, finishing after final bobble with ch1, miss 1 st, 1htr into last st, fasten off B. *(21(23:26) bobbles)*
Row 4: Join in A, ch1, 1dc into same place, *2dc into ch 1 space, 1dc into top of next bobble; rep from * to end of rnd, finishing with 1dc into final bobble, 2dc into ch 3 space, 1dc into 2nd ch of ch 3, turn. *(67(73:82) sts)*
Row 5: Ch3 (counts as 1 tr), miss st at base of ch 3, 1tr into foll st and into each st to end of row.
Small(medium)
Row 6: Ch1, 1dc into same place, 1dc into every st to end of row, turn. *(67(73) sts)*
Large
Row 6: As for small(medium), except in or around the centre of the back work 2dc into 1 st to increase the stitch count by 1. *(83 sts)*

Choosing yarn

Blue Sky Fibers Melange yarn is divine. It has a gorgeous squishiness to it and beautiful flecks of colour that give the cardigan an extra level of interest.

All sizes cont

Row 7: Rep row 3. *(32(35:40) bobbles)*

Row 8: Rep row 4. *(100(109:124) sts)*

Row 9: Rep row 5.

Medium

Row 10: Ch1, 1dc into same place, 1dc into every st to end of row, turn. *(101(109) sts)*

Small(large)

Row 10: As for medium, except in or around the centre of the back work 2dc into 1 st to increase the stitch count by 1. *(101(125) sts)*

All sizes cont

Row 11: Rep row 3. *(49(53:61) bobbles)*

Medium(large)

Row 12: Join in A, ch1, 1dc into same place, *2dc into ch 1 space, 1dc into top of next bobble, 1dc into next ch 1 space, 1dc into top of foll bobble; rep from * to end of row. *(136(156) sts)*

Small

Row 12: As for medium(large), except in the centre of the back in one pattern rep only, work 1dc into ch 1 space in place of 2dc, this will give an odd number of stitches at end of row, turn. *(125 sts)*

All sizes cont

Row 13: Rep row 5.

Small

Row 14: Ch1, 1dc into same place, 1dc into every st to end of row, turn. *(125(137) sts)*

Medium(large)

Row 14: As for small(medium), except in or around the centre of the back work 2dc into 1 st to increase the stitch count by 1. *(137(157) sts)*

Row 15: Rep row 3. *(61(67:77) bobbles)*

Row 16: Ch1, 1dc into same place, *2dc into ch 1 space, 1dc into top of next bobble, 1dc into next ch 1 space, 1dc into top of foll bobble; rep from * to end of row.

Row 17: Rep row 5. *(156(171:196) sts)*

DIVIDE FOR THE BODY AND SLEEVES

BODY

Row 1: Ch1, 1dc into same place and 1dc into each of foll 20(22:25) sts, miss next 35(38:44) sts (this will be worked later and is first sleeve), 1dc into each of next 44(49:56) sts, miss foll 35(38:44) sts (second sleeve), 1dc into each of final 21(23:26) sts (the ch 3 counts as last st), turn. *(86(95:108) sts)*

Small(large)

Row 2: Ch3 (counts as 1 tr), miss st at base of ch 3, 1tr into next st and into every st to reach approx. the middle st, 2tr in this st, then cont working 1tr into every st to end of row, turn. *(87(109) sts)*

Medium

Row 2: Ch3 (counts as 1 tr), miss st at base of ch 3, 1tr into next st and into every st to end of row, turn. *(95 sts)*

All sizes cont

Row 3: Ch3 (counts as 1 tr), miss st at base of ch 3, 1tr into next st and into every st to end of row, turn.

Rep row 3, 4(5:6) more times.

Next row: Ch1, 1dc into same place, 1dc into every st, to end of row, turn.

Next row: Ch3 (counts as 1 htr, ch 1), miss st at the base of ch 2 and foll st, *BOBBLE into next st, ch1, miss next st; rep from * to end of row, finishing after final bobble with ch1, miss 1 st, 1htr into last st.

Next row: Ch1, 1dc into same place, *1dc into next ch 1 space, 1dc into top of foll bobble; rep from * to end of row, turn.

Next row: Ch3 (counts as 1 tr), miss st at base of ch 3, 1tr into next st and into every st to end of row, turn.

Next row: Ch1, 1dc into same place, 1dc into next st and into every st to end of row, fasten off.

Round 2: Ch3 (counts as 1 tr), tr2tog over next 2 sts, 1tr into next st and into every st to last 2 sts, tr2tog, join with a sl st to top of ch 3, turn. *(33(36:42) sts)*

Round 3: Rep rnd 2, fasten off if working small size. *(31(34:40) sts)*

For medium and large sizes, rep round 1, 1(2) more times, fasten off.

Round 4: Join in B at the underarm, ch2, htr2tog into same place as ch2, yrh, *ch1, miss 1 st, bobble into next st; rep from * to end of rnd, missing 2 sts at end of rnd for the SMALL size, join with a sl st to top of first bobble, do not turn.

Round 5: Sl st into next ch 1 space, ch2, htr2tog in this ch 1 space, *ch1, BOBBLE into next ch 1 space; rep from * to end of rnd, join with a sl st to top of first bobble, fasten off B.

Round 6: Join in A, ch1, 1 dc into same place, work 1 dc into every bobble and ch sp to end of rnd, join with a sl st to first dc, do not turn.

Round 7: Ch1, 1dc into same place, 1dc into next st, *ch3, sl st into 3rd ch from hook (picot made), miss next st, 1dc into each of foll 2 sts; rep from * to end of rnd, join with a sl st to first dc made, fasten off.

Rep for second sleeve.

TO MAKE UP

Weave in ends (see page 125).
Sew the buttons to the button band.

BUTTONHOLE BAND

Row 1: Join A to the bottom of RH side, work a row of dc evenly up the RH edge, (as a general rule working 2dc along the side of every tr and 1dc in every dc and htr).

Row 2: As row 1, but at row of trebles between bobble row 3 and 7, ch2, miss 1 st (first buttonhole made), cont working 1dc into every st to tr row between bobble row 7 and 11, ch2, miss 1 st (second buttonhole made), cont working 1dc into every st to tr row between bobble rows 11 and 15, ch2, miss 1 st (third buttonhole made), then cont working 1dc into every st to the bottom, turn.

Row 3: Work 1dc into every st to end of row, fasten off.

BUTTON BAND

Row 1: Join A to the top of LH side, work a row of dc evenly down the LH edge, (as a general rule working 2dc along the side of every tr and 1dc in every dc and htr).

Rows 2–3: Work 1dc into every st to end of row. Fasten off.

SLEEVE

Rejoin the yarn at the underarm of one sleeve with the RS facing.

Round 1: Ch3 (counts as 1 tr), miss st at the base of ch 3, 1tr into next st and into every st to end of rnd, join with a sl st to top of ch 3, turn. *35(38:44 sts)*

Be careful not to work into the stitches that you have already worked in the body, this is very easy to do, so it is probably best to count if in doubt!

TIGER *Toy*

More of a Tigger than a scary Tiger, I love the way this gorgeous feline can give you a cuddle with his squidgy arms, and sit by you or on you with his little legs dangling beneath him! Rather like the owl (see page 108), this toy is crocheted from the bottom up in the round. The head is separate and all his appendages are added once his body and head are stuffed. So when you come to create his features, you can experiment with placing the eyes and muzzle to get them just right, and add your own personal touches.

Yarn

Mrs Moon Plump (80% superfine merino wool, 20% baby alpaca) super-chunky (super-bulky) yarn, 100g (3½oz), 70m (76yd) skeins

2 skeins in Earl Grey (A)

2 skeins in Marmalade (B)

Small amount of Pavlova (C)

Other materials

Toy stuffing

Hook and equipment

8mm (US L/11) crochet hook

Large tapestry needle

Size

37cm (14½in) high when sitting

Tension

7 tr sts and 4 tr rows over 10cm (4in) using 8mm (US L/11) crochet hook

Abbreviations

See page 114

BODY

Note that you need to start stuffing the body as you start to decrease. Do not fasten off yarn between rows but carry it up on the inside of the body.

Using A, ch4, join with a sl st to form a ring.

Round 1: Ch3 (counts as 1 tr), work 11 tr into the ring, join with sl st to top of ch 3. *(12 tr)*

Round 2: Join in B, ch3 (counts as 1 tr), 1tr into same place, 2tr into next tr and into every tr to end of rnd, join rnd with sl st to top of ch 3, do not turn. *(24 sts)*

Round 3: Change to A, ch3 (counts as 1 tr), 1tr into same place, *1tr into foll st, 2tr into next st; rep from * to end of rnd, finish with 1tr in last st, join with a sl st to top of ch 3, do not turn. *(36 sts)*

Round 4: Using B and working in BLO, ch3 (counts as 1 tr), 1tr into next st and into every st to end of rnd, join rnd with a sl st to top of ch 3, do not turn.

Round 5: Using A, ch3 (counts as 1 tr), 1tr into next st and into every st to end of rnd, join rnd with a sl st to top of ch 3, do not turn.

Rounds 6–13: Rep rnd 5, changing colour every row.

Round 14: Using A, ch3 (counts as 1 tr), 1tr into next st, tr2tog, *1tr into each of next 2 sts, tr2tog; rep from * to end of rnd, join with a sl st to top of ch 3, do not turn. *(27 sts)*

Round 15: Using B, ch3 (counts as 1 tr), tr2tog, *1tr into foll st, tr2tog; rep from * to end of rnd, join with a sl st to top of ch 3, do not turn. *(18 sts)*

Round 16: Using A, ch3 (counts as 1 tr), tr2tog, tr2tog; rep from * to last st, 1tr in last st, join with a sl st to top of ch 3, do not turn.

Round 17: Using B, rep rnd 16.

Make sure body is nicely stuffed and fasten off.

HEAD

Note that you need to stuff the head as you work it.

Do not fasten off yarn between rows but bring it up on the inside of the head.

Using A, ch4, join with a sl st to form a ring.

Round 1: Ch3, (counts as 1 tr), 11 tr into ring, join with a sl st to top of ch 3, do not turn. *(12 sts)*

Round 2: Using B, ch3 (counts as 1 tr), 1tr into same place, 2tr into every st to end of rnd, join with a sl st to top of ch 3, do not turn. *(24 sts)*

Round 3: Using A, ch3 (counts as 1 tr), 1 tr into same place, *1tr into each of next 2 sts, 2tr into foll st; rep from * finishing with 1 tr into each of last 2 sts, join with a sl st to top of ch 3, do not turn. *(32 sts)*

Round 4: Using B, ch3 (counts as 1 tr), 1tr into next st and into every st to end of rnd, join with a sl st to top of ch 3, do not turn.

Rounds 5–8: Rep rnd 4, changing colour every row.

Round 9: Using A, ch2 (counts as 1 htr), 1htr into next st, htr2tog, *1htr into each of next 2 sts, htr2tog; rep from * finishing with htr2tog, join with a sl st to top of ch 2, do not turn. *(24 sts)*

Round 10: Using B, ch2 (counts as 1 htr), htr2tog, *1 htr into next st, htr2tog; rep from * finishing with htr2tog, join with sl st to top of ch 2, do not turn. *(16 sts)*

Round 11: Using A, ch2 (counts as 1 htr), htr2tog over next 2 sts, cont working htr2tog to end of rnd, finish with 1htr, join rnd with a sl st to top of ch 2, do not turn. *(9 sts)*

Round 12: Using B, ch2 (counts as 1 htr), htr2tog over next 2 sts, cont working htr2tog, to end of rnd, finish with 1htr, join rnd with a sl st to top of ch 2, fasten off.

LEG AND FOOT

(Make 2)

Using C, ch2.

Round 1: 8dc into 2nd ch from hook, join with a sl st to first dc made, do not turn. You may want to mark the first dc as it is not that easy to see! *(8 sts)*

Round 2: Ch1, 2dc into same place, 2dc into every st to end of rnd, join with a sl st to top of first dc made, fasten off. *(16 sts)*

Round 3: Join in B, ch1, 1dc into same place, 1dc into next st and into every st to end of rnd, join with a sl st to first dc made, do not turn. *(16 dc)*

Round 4: Rep rnd 3.

Round 5: Join in A, ch1, 1dc into same place, 1dc into next st, *dc2tog over next 2 sts, 1dc into each of foll 2 sts; rep from * to last 2 sts, dc2tog, join with a sl st to top of first dc made, do not turn. *(12 sts)*

Round 6: Rep rnd 5. *(9 sts)*

Round 7: Using B, ch1, 1dc into same place, 1dc into next st and into every st to end of rnd, join with a sl st to top of first dc made, do not turn. *(9 sts)*

Round 8: Rep rnd 7.

Fasten off.

Stuff each leg. The ends remain open.

ARM

(Make 2)

Using C, ch2.

Round 1: 8dc into the 2nd ch from hook, join with a sl st to first dc made, fasten off. *(8 sts)*

Round 2: Join in B, ch1, 1dc into same place, 1dc into next st and into every st to end of rnd, join with a sl st to top of first dc made, do not turn. *(8 sts)*

Rounds 3–17: Rep rnd 2, changing colour every 2 rnds. Stuff the arms as you go. The ends remain open.

MUZZLE

Using C, ch4.

Round 1: (3dtr, 3tr, ch1, 1dtr, ch1, 3tr, 3dtr, ch2) all into 4th ch from hook, sl st into centre of muzzle, you should end up with a heart shape, fasten off.

NOSE

Using A, ch4.

Round 1: 1dc into 2nd and 3rd ch from hook, sl st into 4th ch, turn and work down the other side of the chain by sl st into what was the 4th ch again, 1dc into each of next 2 ch, 1 sl st into final ch, pull tight (should look like a triangle), fasten off.

EYE

(Make 2)

Using C, ch2.

Round 1: Work 8dc into the 2nd ch from hook, pull tight and fasten off. Using A, embroider a pupil.

EAR

(Make 2)

Using C, ch4.

Round 1: 1dc into 2nd and 3rd ch from hook, sl st into 4th ch, turn and work down the other side of the chain by sl st into what was the 4th ch again, 1dc into each of next 2 ch, 1 sl st into final ch, pull tight (should look like a triangle), fasten off.

Round 2: Join in B, ch1, 1dc into same place, work 1 dc into next st, 3dc into end st, turn, work 1dc into each of next 2 sts.

Round 3: Join in A, ch1, 1dc into same place, 1dc into each of next 2 sts, 1dc into next st, ch3, 1dc into next st and into each of the final 2 sts, fasten off.

TAIL

Work as for arm, but work 25 rounds in total.

TO MAKE UP

Weave in ends on all parts (see page 125).
Sew head onto the body. Then sew on the legs, arms and tail using the photo as a guide. Sew the facial features and sew a line up from the bottom of the muzzle to the nose.

GRANNY RECTANGLE *Bolero*

This is a great first garment project for someone new to crochet, and is totally adorable! It's perfect to keep a little girl warm when she's wearing her favourite party dress, and unlike most cardigans, it adds something really special rather than detracting from the main event. You can make it as big or small as you want by just adding or taking away rounds. Also, of course, you can jazz up or down the colour combinations – I think that a plain colour would look lovely, too!

Yarn

Mrs Moon Plump DK (80% superfine merino wool, 20% baby alpaca) double knitting (light-worsted-weight) yarn, 50g (1¾oz), 115m (125yd) skeins
  1 skein in Fondant Fancy (A)
  1 skein in Rhubarb Crumble (B)
Mrs Moon Fluff (80% kid mohair, 20% silk) lace weight (fingering) yarn, 25g (¾oz), 200m (218yd) skeins
  1 ball in Rhubarb Crumble (C)

Hook and equipment

4.5mm (US G/6 or H/8) crochet hook
Large tapestry needle

Size

To fit: 5–6(6–7:7–8) years
Finished measurements
Width (before seaming): 38(44:48)cm (15(17¼:18¾)in)
Length (nape to hem): 28(34:38)cm (11(13½:15)in)

Tension

4 groups of 3 tr sts (including 4 ch spaces) and 9 rows over 10cm (4in) using 4.5mm (US G/6 or H/8) crochet hook

Abbreviations

See page 114

RECTANGLE

Using A, ch18.

Round 1: 1tr into 4th ch from hook, 1tr into next ch, *ch1, miss 1 ch, 1tr into each of next 3 ch; rep from * twice more, ch2, 3tr into last ch, ch2 (you are now moving round to the other side of the foundation chain), 1tr into each of next 3 ch (these already have trebles in on the side you have just completed), **ch1, miss 1 ch, 1tr into each of next 3 ch; rep from ** twice more, (you should now be working in the st at the base of ch 3), ch2, 3tr into same st, ch2, join the rnd with a sl st to top of ch 3, do not turn.

Round 2: Sl st into each of next two tr and into ch 1 space, ch3 (counts as 1 tr), 2tr into same ch 1 space, (ch1, 3tr) into next two ch 1 spaces, ch1, (3tr, ch2, 3tr) into ch 2 space, ch1, (3tr, ch2, 3tr) into foll ch 2 space, *ch1, 3tr into next ch 1 space; rep from * twice more, ch1, (3tr, ch2, 3tr) into next ch 2 space, ch1, (3tr, ch2, 3tr) into final ch 2 space, ch1, join with a sl st to top of ch 3, fasten off A, do not turn.

Round 3: Join B to top right ch 2 corner space, ch3 (counts as 1 tr), (2tr, ch2, 3tr) into same ch 2 space, (ch1, 3tr) into next four ch 1 spaces, *ch1, (3tr, ch2, 3tr) into ch 2 space, ch1, 3tr into next ch 1 space; rep from * once more, (ch1, 3tr) into next three ch 1 spaces, ch1, (3tr, ch2, 3tr) into last corner ch 2 space, ch1, 3tr into last ch 1 space, join with a sl st to top of ch 3, do not turn.

Rounds 4–13: Rep rnd 3, changing colour every 2 rnds, beginning with 2 rnds of A. Work (3tr, ch2, 3tr) into every

Fluffy

The little bit of Fluff around the openings of this bolero makes it really special, and the yarn is so soft that it won't irritate sensitive skin, as some mohairs can.

ch 2 corner space and 3tr into every ch 1 side space, all groups of tr must be separated by ch 1 (except the ch 2 in each corner).

When starting a new round but keeping same colour, always slip stitch over next 2 tr and into next space as every round must start in a space. Ch3 at start of all new rounds and that ch 3 counts as 1 tr.

6–7 years (7–8 years)

Work 2(4) more rnds.

Alternatively measure the bolero against the child and increase as necessary.

TO MAKE UP

Weave in ends (see page 125).

Sew up the bolero by folding it in half lengthways, then put a couple of stitches in last tr on either end of the long end.

TRIM

Round 1: Using C, work one complete round of dc around the inside edge and each sleeve edge, working 1dc into every tr and 1dc into every ch1 space.

Round 2 (picot): Work around inside edge and both sleeve edges alike, join C to any dc from rnd 1, ch1, 1dc into same place, 1dc into each of next two sts, *ch3, sl st into 3rd ch from hook (picot made), 1dc into each of next 3 sts; rep from * to end of rnd, join with a sl st to first dc, fasten off.

Starting the rectangle

You work around both sides of the foundation chain to set up the granny rectangle, adding a group of 3 tr at each end. You really don't need to worry too much about where you put these end sts, just squeeze them into the last ch; all will work out on the following rounds!

GIANT *Cuddly owl*

Warning: this owl is so cute, you won't want to give him away.... bear this in mind before you start making him! He is a very simple construction, crocheted from the bottom up in the round and then the crown, eyes, ears, wings and feet are added afterwards. The simple stitches give him a texture and look that is totally adorable! When it comes to stuffing the owl, I've gone for a very soft, squidgy feel making him perfect for a child, but you can do as you please: you can even weight him and use him as a doorstop. Personally though, I think he is best for cuddling – squashy and soft and very, very cute!

Yarn

Mrs Moon Plump (80% superfine merino wool, 20% baby alpaca) super-chunky (super-bulky) yarn, 100g (3½oz), 70m (76yd) skeins
  3 skeins in Earl Grey (A)
  3 skeins in Pavlova (B)
  Small amount of Marmalade (feet and beak) (C)
Mrs Moon Plump DK (80% superfine merino wool, 20% baby alpaca) double knitting (light-worsted-weight) yarn, 50g (1¾oz), 115m (125yd) skeins
Small amounts of Pavlova, Marmalade and Earl Grey for the eyes

Other materials

Toy stuffing

Hooks and equipment

8mm (US L/11) crochet hook and 12mm (US O/17) crochet hooks
Large tapestry needle

Size

30cm (12in) high, 108cm (42½in) circumference

Tension

9 dc sts and 10 dc rows over 10cm (4in) using 8mm (US L/11) crochet hook

Abbreviations

PUFF = htr3tog in same space, yrh and pull through to secure.
PUFF1 = This is worked at the beginning of the rnd to incorporate the turning ch: htr2tog in same space, yrh and pull through to secure.
See also page 114

BODY

Using 8mm (US L/11) hook and A, ch6, join with a sl st to form a ring.
Round 1: Ch3 (counts as 1 tr), work 15tr into ring. *(16 tr)*
Round 2: Ch3 (counts as 1 tr), 1tr into same place, 2tr into each tr, join with a sl st to top of ch 3. *(32 sts)*
Round 3: Ch3 (counts as 1 tr), 1tr into same place, 1tr into next st, *2tr into next st, 1tr into next st; rep from * to end, join with a sl st to top of ch 3. *(48 sts)*

Round 4: Ch3 (counts as 1 tr), 1tr into same place, 1tr into each of next 2 sts, *2tr into next st, 1tr into each of next 2 sts; rep from * to end, join with a sl st to top of ch 3. *(64 sts)*
Round 5: Ch 3 (counts as 1 tr), 1tr into same place, 1tr into each of next 3 tr, *2tr into next st, 1tr into each of next 3 tr; rep from * to end, join with a sl st to top of ch 3. *(80 sts: base of owl complete)*
Note that you must weave in any ends on the inside of the owl as you crochet, and you will also need to start stuffing him as he grows.

Round 6: Ch1, dc2tog (working 1st dc of dc2tog into same st as ch1), 1dc into each of next 38 sts, dc2tog, 1dc in every st to end of rnd, join with sl st. *(78 sts)*

Round 7: Ch3 (counts as 1 tr), 2tr into same place, *miss 2 dc, 1 dc into next st, miss 2 dc, 5tr into next st; rep from * to end, finishing with 2tr into st at base of ch 3, then to complete the 5tr group join with sl st to top of ch 3. Do not fasten off, but carry yarn A up the inside for rnd 9. *(13 shells)*

Round 8: Join B to where you left off in the previous rnd, ch1, 1dc into same place (middle tr of 5tr), *miss 2 tr, 5tr in next dc, miss 2 tr, 1dc into next tr; rep from * to end of rnd, finishing with 5tr in last dc, join with a sl st to 1st dc. Do not fasten off, but carry yarn B up the inside for rnd 10.

Round 9: Pick up A, ch3, 2tr into same place, *1dc into 3rd tr of next shell, 5tr into next dc; rep from * to end, finishing by working 2tr into same place as first 3 tr, join with sl st to top of ch 3. Rep rnds 8–9 until 17 rnds of shells are completed.

SHAPE TOP OF BODY

A note on decreasing: A shell decrease starts at the top of the shell (from the previous row), on the dc as folls: 1dc into 3rd tr of shell, dc into next dc, dc into 3rd tr next of shell, now work a normal shell into next dc (1 shell decreased). You always need to start a decrease on the dc at the top of a shell, so if you are not in this place at the end of a rnd, you must sl st into the first 3 tr of next shell and then work the decrease.

Finish stuffing the owl as you decrease rows.

Round 18: You should be on a B rnd; starting with a dc at the top of a shell, ch1, *1dc into same place, 1dc into next dc, 1dc into the middle tr of next shell, work 2 normal shells, then one shell decrease; rep from * – so working one shell decrease followed by two normal shells – finish with a decrease, then join rnd with a sl st to top of first dc made. *(8 shells, 5 decreases: note that it really doesn't matter how neat this looks as long as it is reasonably even as it will be covered by the ears/top.)*

Round 19: Change to A, *dc3tog, work one shell decrease, work 1 normal shell; rep from * to end, finishing with dc3tog, join rnd with a sl st to top of 1st dc3tog.

Round 20: Cont in A, ch1, then cont to decrease by working tr2togs and working 1 dc in top of remaining shells to decrease them. Do not sl st to join but cont to work in a spiral, working tr2togs until top is covered. Switch to dc2togs in final rnds if necessary to close hole.

Fasten off and weave in ends.

EARS/TOP

Using 8mm (US L/11) hook and B, ch22.

Row 1: Work 1 dc into 2nd ch from hook and in every ch to end of row, turn.

Row 2: Ch1, 1dc into same place and into every st to end of row, turn.

Rep row 2, 21 times more, or until work is square.

Fasten off.

EDGING/EARS

Join in A, ch1, 1dc into same place, 1dc into next st and into every st to last st, in last st of this row work the first ear as folls: ch3, sl st into the corner, ch5, sl st into the corner, ch3, sl st into next st, cont working a row of dc evenly along the edge, 3dc into next corner, and work dc evenly along bottom edge, work another ear into next corner, work a row of dc evenly along the final edge, 3dc into corner, fasten off yarn and weave in ends. Position this piece onto the top of the owl's head with the ears either side of the centre and sew in place, pinching the ears and sewing across the base of them, but leaving the picot edges sticking out (see photograph).

EYE

(Make 2)

Using 8mm (US L/11) hook and Plump DK throughout, using Earl Grey, ch5 and join with a sl st to form a ring, being careful not to twist the chain.

Round 1: Ch3 (counts as 1 tr), work 15 more tr into the ring, join rnd to top of ch 3 with a sl st, fasten off A. *(16 sts)*

Round 2: Join Marmalade to any tr, ch2, PUFF1 into same place, PUFF into next tr and into every tr to end of rnd, join with a sl st to top of the PUFF1, fasten off Marmalade. *(16 Puffs)*

Round 3: Join Pavlova to any space between the PUFFs, ch3 (counts as 1 tr), tr3tog, ch1, *tr4tog into next space, ch1; rep from * to end of rnd, finishing with a sl st into top of tr3tog, fasten off.

BEAK

Using C, ch8.

Row 1: 1dc into 2nd ch from hook, dc into each ch to end of row. *(7 sts)*

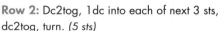

Row 2: Dc2tog, 1dc into each of next 3 sts, dc2tog, turn. *(5 sts)*

Row 3: Dc2tog, 1dc into next st, dc2tog, turn. *(3 sts)*

Row 4: Dc3tog, fasten off.

WING

(Make 2)

Using 12mm (US O/17) hook and one strand each of A and B held together, ch10.

Row 1: 1dc into 5th ch from hook, ch5, 1dc into the foll ch, *ch5, 1dc into next ch; rep from * to end of row, fasten off.

FOOT

(Make 2)

Using C, ch4.

Row 1: Sl st into 2nd ch from hook, then into each of next 2 ch, ch3, *sl st into 2nd and 3rd ch from hook and then into first ch made (of the ch 4), ch3; rep from * once more, fasten off.

TO MAKE UP

Weave in ends (see page 125).

Using image as a guide, position eyes, beak, wings and feet on your owl and sew into place.

CHILD'S RETRO *Blanket*

This is a fun and easy absolute beginner project – once you know how to make a treble, you are ready to go! It is excellent in-front-of-the-television crochet, and if you change colours every two rows, as I have, it seems to grow really quickly. As well as a written pattern, there is a chart to help you work this project. You always start the next row one stitch in from the row below, either by slip stitching in one stitch or, if you are starting a new colour, joining it in the second stitch. This creates a slightly staggered edge that I've disguised with a pretty border. I'd really recommend weaving the ends in as you go to avoid hours of weaving in once the blanket is (almost) finished!

Yarn

Rooster Almerino DK (50% baby alpaca, 50% merino wool) double knitting (light-worsted-weight) yarn, 50g (1¾oz), 113m (124yd) balls

- 2 balls in Gooseberry 207 (A)
- 2 balls in Strawberry Cream 203 (B)
- 2 balls in Grape 204 (C)
- 2 balls in Custard 210 (D)
- 2 balls in Cherry 213 (E)
- 2 balls in Hazelnut 202 (F)
- 2 balls in Smoothie 209 (G)
- 2 balls in Damson 214 (H)
- 2 balls in Starfish 218 (J)

Hook and equipment

4mm (US F/5 or G/6) crochet hook
Large tapestry needle

Size

147 x 81cm (58 x 32in)

Tension

15 dc sts and 12 dc rows over 10cm (4in) using 4mm (US F/5 or G/6) crochet hook
17 tr sts and 9 tr rows over 10cm (4in) using 4mm (US F/5 or G/6) crochet hook, measured over chevron pattern

Abbreviations

See page 114

BLANKET

Using A, ch247 loosely.

Row 1: 1tr into 4th ch from hook (first 3 ch count as 1 tr), 1tr into each of next 3 ch, 3tr into next ch (this is the increase), 1tr into each of next 5 ch, miss next 2 ch (this is the decrease), 1tr into each of next 5 ch, *3tr into next ch, 1tr into each of next 5 ch, miss next 2 ch, 1tr into each of next 5 ch; rep from * to last 6 ch, 3tr into next ch, 1tr into each of last 5 ch.

Row 2: Sl st into first and second st (this is where next row starts from), ch3 (counts as 1tr), 1tr into each of next 4 tr, *3tr into next tr (this is the middle tr of increase in previous row), 1tr into each of next 5 tr, miss next 2 tr (these are the bottom two sts of decrease in previous row), 1tr into each of next 5 tr; rep from * to last 6 tr (not including 3 ch), 3tr into next tr, 1 tr into each of last 5 tr, turn (do not work into the ch 3).

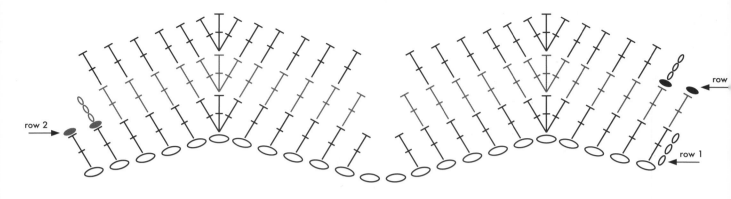

row 2

row 1

row

Key

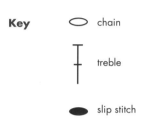

○ chain

┼ treble

● slip stitch

Rows 3–72: Rep row 2, changing colour on this row and every following second row. When changing colour on a new row, join the new yarn to the second st and ch 3; you do not need to sl st as you are where you need to be to start the row.
Fasten off.

BORDER

There is yarn left over to do the trim in colours of your choice; I have used B and D.

Row 1: Using B, work one row of dc evenly along each edge, ensuring the final stitch count is a multiple of 3 (as a general rule work 2dc into the length of 1 tr), turn.

Row 2: *Ch5, miss 2 dc, sl st into next st; rep from * to end. Fasten off.

Row 3: Join D to first ch 5 loop, *ch5, sl st into 3rd ch from hook, ch2, 1dc into next ch 5 loop; rep from * to end. (A basic picot or shell pattern would also look lovely.)

TO MAKE UP

Weave in ends (see page 125).

Creating chevrons

Although it looks more complicated, the blanket simply involves rows of trebles with very simple increases (working three stitches into one place) and decreases (missing two stitches). It is also very easy to see if you have gone wrong, as the increases and decreases always fall in the same place. The decreases make very attractive holes in the blanket that are a feature of a chevron as opposed to a ripple, where there are no holes at all.

Changing size

I have made this blanket wide and quite short to go over the bottom of a child's bed, but as the stitch pattern is simply a multiple of 13, it is easy to go up or down in size. Make the chain slightly looser than you require as the chevrons shrink it slightly.

Techniques

On the following pages you'll find useful crochet techniques for making the projects in this book. From the basics of holding the hook and yarn and making your first stitches, through to changing colours neatly and finishing your work beautifully, each method is illustrated and explained.

Abbreviations

[ ]	square parentheses indicate a repeat
*	asterisk indicates where to repeat from
approx.	approximately
BLO	back loop only
ch	chain
cm	centimetre(s)
cont	continue
dc	double crochet
dc2tog	double crochet 2 stitches together
foll(s)	follow(s)(ing)
g	gram(s)
htr	half treble crochet
htr2(3)tog	half treble crochet 2(3) stitches together
m	metre(s)
patt	pattern
rep	repeat
RS	right side of work
sl st	slip stitch
st(s)	stitch(es)
tch	turning chain
tr	treble crochet
tr2(3)tog	treble crochet 2(3) stitches together

WS	wrong side of work
yrh	yarn round hook

Crochet stitch conversions

Crochet stitches are worked in the same way in both the USA and the UK, but the stitch names are not the same, and identical names are used for different stitches.

Below is a list of the UK terms used in this book, and the equivalent US terms.

UK TERM	US TERM
double crochet (dc)	single crochet (sc)
half treble (htr)	half double crochet (hdc)
treble (tr)	double crochet (dc)
double treble (dtr)	treble (tr)
triple treble (trtr)	double treble (dtr)
miss	skip
tension	gauge
yarn round hook (yrh)	yarn over hook (yoh)

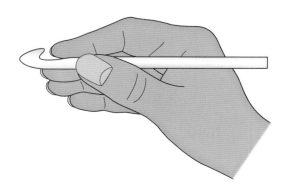

Holding the hook

Hold the hook in a similar way to a pencil. Do not grip it hard, and keep it balanced in your hand with the shaft resting in the crook between your index finger and your thumb.

Holding the yarn

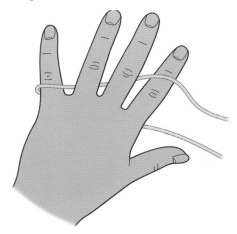

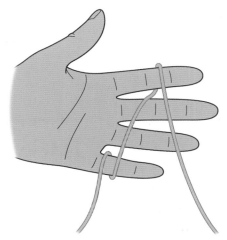

1 Hold the yarn in your left hand. Precisely how you wrap the yarn around your fingers to tension it will vary depending on what feels comfortable for you. For a looser hold, wrap the yarn over your little finger, under the two middle fingers and then over your index finger.

2 For a tighter hold, wrap the yarn right around your little finger, then under and over the other fingers as in Step 1.

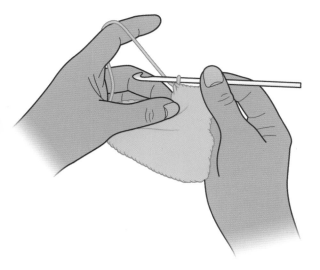

Holding the hook and yarn together

Keep your left index finger – with the yarn draped over it – held up, and grip the work between the middle finger and thumb of your left hand, holding it just below the crochet hook.

With the hook pointing upwards, catch the yarn from below. Turn the hook so it faces downwards and pull the new yarn loop through the stitch or the loop on the hook. As you draw the new loop through, relax the yarn on your index finger to allow the loop to stay loose. If you tense your index finger, the loop on the hook will be pulled too tight for you to draw the new loop through.

Some left-handers learn to crochet like right-handers, but others learn with everything reversed – with the hook in their left hand and the yarn in the right. Try both ways to see which is most comfortable fo you.

Making a slip knot

A slip knot is the starting point for crochet.

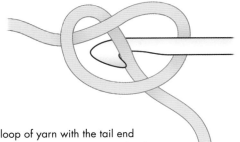 

1 Make a loop of yarn with the tail end going under the circle. With a crochet hook, pull a loop through the circle.

2 Slip the loop along the hook and pull the tail gently to make a loose loop on the hook.

Chain (ch)

A foundation chain is needed for most projects, and chains can be made within a piece of crochet fabric.

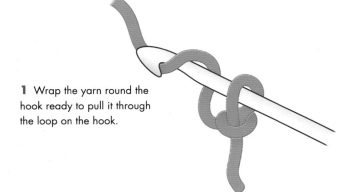

1 Wrap the yarn round the hook ready to pull it through the loop on the hook.

2 Pull the yarn through, creating a new loop on the hook. Continue in this way to create a chain of the required number of stitches.

Chain ring

The starting point for most projects worked in the round.

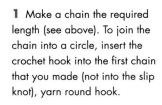 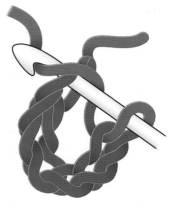 

1 Make a chain the required length (see above). To join the chain into a circle, insert the crochet hook into the first chain that you made (not into the slip knot), yarn round hook.

2 Pull the yarn through the chain and through the loop on the hook at the same time, creating a slip stitch to join the chain into a circle.

Working into a stitch

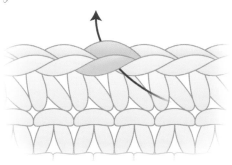

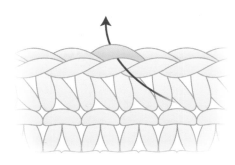

A stitch has two loops lying across the top of it. Unless otherwise directed, insert the hook under both of these loops.

Some projects in this book ask you to work into the back loop (BLO) of a stitch. To do this, insert the hook between the front and the back loop, picking up the back loop only.

Working into a chain space (ch-sp)

A chain space is the space between stitches that has been made under a chain in the previous round or row.

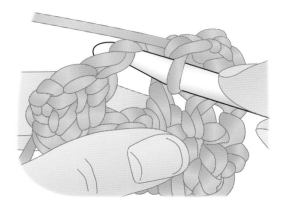

1 Insert the hook under the chain, not through the stitches that make it. Wrap the yarn round the hook and pull it back through the chain space.

Slip stitch (sl st)

A slip stitch doesn't create any height. It can be used to move to a different position in the work, or to join elements together.

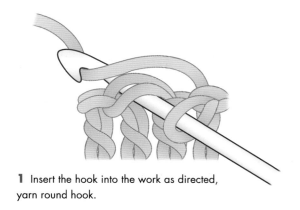

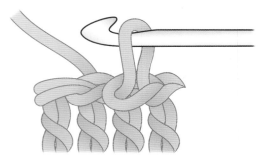

1 Insert the hook into the work as directed, yarn round hook.

2 Pull the yarn through both the work and the loop on the hook at the same time, so that there is just one loop left on the hook.

Double crochet (dc)

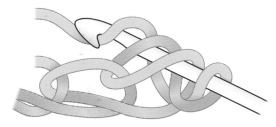

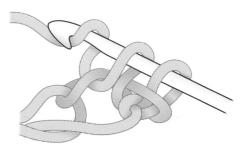

1 Insert the hook into the work as directed, yarn round hook, and pull the yarn through the work only. There are two loops on the hook.

2 Yarn round hook again, and pull through the two loops on the hook, so that there is just one loop left on the hook. One double crochet stitch completed.

Making rows and rounds

When making straight rows you turn the work at the end of each row. To start the next row, you make a turning chain (tch) to create the height needed for the stitch you will use.

Double crochet = 1 chain

Half treble crochet = 2 chains

Treble crochet = 3 chains

When working in rounds the work is not turned, so you are always working from one side. Depending on the pattern you are working, a 'round' can be square.

Start each round by making a turning chain as for working in rows. Work the required stitches to complete the round. At the end of the round, slip stitch into the top of the chain to close the round.

If you are working in a spiral, you do not need a turning chain. After completing the base ring, place a stitch marker in the first stitch and then continue to crochet around. When you have made a round and reached the point where the stitch marker is, work this stitch, take out the stitch marker from the previous round and put it back into the first stitch of the new round. A safety pin, or piece of yarn in a contrasting colour, makes a good stitch marker.

Half treble crochet (htr)

1 Wrap the yarn round the hook before inserting the hook into the work as directed.

2 Yarn round hook again, and pull through the work. There are three loops on the hook.

3 Yarn round hook and pull the yarn through all three loops, so that there is just one loop left on the hook. One half treble crochet stitch completed.

Treble crochet (tr)

1 Wrap the yarn round the hook before inserting the hook into the work as directed. Put the hook through the work, yarn round hook again and pull through the work. There are three loops on the hook.

2 Yarn round hook again, pull the yarn through the first two loops on the hook. There are two loops left on the hook.

3 Yarn round hook again, and pull the yarn through two loops again, so that there is just one loop left on the hook. One treble crochet stitch completed.

Increasing

To increase, make two or three stitches into one stitch or space from the previous row. The illustration shows a treble crochet increase being made.

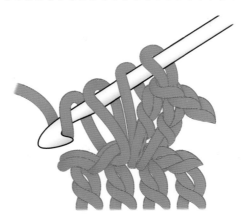

Decreasing

You can decrease by either missing the next stitch and continuing to crochet, or by crocheting two or more stitches together.

Double crochet two stitches together (dc2tog)

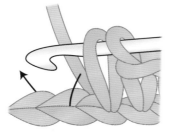

1 Insert the hook into the work, yarn round hook, and pull the yarn through the work so that there are two loops on the hook. Insert the hook into next stitch, yarn round hook, and pull the yarn through so that there are three loops on the hook.

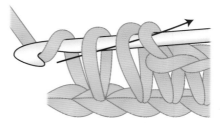

2 Yarn round hook again and pull through all three loops on the hook, so that there is just one loop left on the hook. Two stitches have been worked together to decrease the number of stitches in the row by one.

Half treble crochet two stitches together (htr2tog)

1 The principle is the same as for dc2tog (see above). Make a half treble stitch (see page 119) into the next stitch, but do not pull the final loop through, so there are three loops on the hook. Then repeat the process into the next stitch, so that there are five loops on the hook.

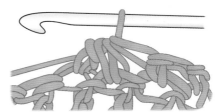

2 Yarn round hook and pull through all five loops on the hook, so that there is just one loop left on the hook. Two stitches have been worked together to decrease the number of stitches in the row by one.

Treble crochet three stitches together (tr3tog)

1 To decrease treble stitches, the principle is the same as for decreasing half trebles (see above). Work each treble, but do not pull the final loop through. After the first treble you will have two loops on the hook, and after the next treble you will have three loops on the hook: for tr2tog, wrap the yarn round the hook and pull through all the loops. For tr3tog, which is the decrease illustrated here, make a final treble so that there are four loops on the hook. Complete the decrease by yarn round hook and pull through all the loops, so that there is just one loop left on the hook. Three stitches have been worked together to decrease the number of stitches in the row by two.

Joining in new yarn

Whether it is a new ball of yarn, or a different colour, you will have to join in yarn for all but the simplest and smallest crochet projects. The method used varies depending on where in the work the yarn needs to be joined in.

Joining into a stitch or space

The method is shown here on a stitch, but the principle is the same for joining into a chain space.

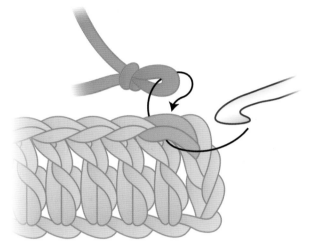

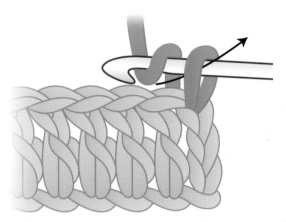

1 Make a slip knot (see page 116) and take it off the hook. Insert the hook into the stitch (or space) the yarn is to be joined to, then put the hook into the slip knot.

2 Yarn round hook, and pull through the slip knot. The yarn is securely joined in. Weave in the tail of yarn from the slip knot (see page 125) after working a row, or once the work is complete.

Joining a new colour at the start of a row

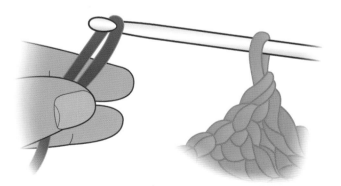

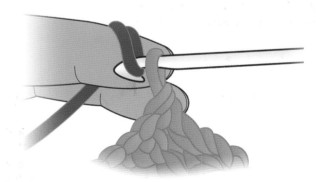

1 Keep the loop of the old yarn on the hook. Drop the old yarn tail and catch the new yarn with the crochet hook.

2 Pull a loop of the new yarn through the loop on the hook, keeping the old loop drawn tight. Start crocheting with the new yarn. Weave in the tail of the old yarn (see page 125) after working a row, or once the work is complete.

Joining a new colour into double crochet

For a neat colour join in the middle of a row or round of double crochet, use this method.

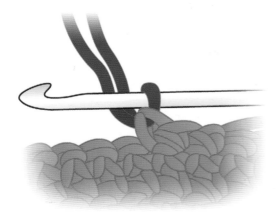 

1 Make a double crochet stitch (see page 118), but do not pull the final loop through, so there are two loops on the hook. Drop the old yarn, catch the new yarn with the hook and pull it through both loops to complete the stitch and join in the new colour at the same time.

2 Continue to crochet with the new yarn. Cut the old yarn leaving a 15cm (6in) tail and weave the tail in (see page 125) after working a row, or once the work is complete.

Joining a new colour into treble crochet

This is the method for a neat colour join in the middle of a row or round of treble crochet.

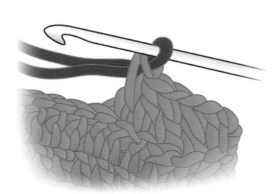 

1 Make a treble crochet stitch (see page 119), but do not pull the final loop through, so there are two loops on the hook. Drop the old yarn, catch the new yarn with the hook and pull it through both loops to complete the stitch and join in the new colour at the same time.

2 Continue to crochet with the new yarn. Cut the old yarn leaving a 15cm (6in) tail and weave the tail in (see page 125) after working a row, or once the work is complete.

Seaming with double crochet

I prefer to join seams with crochet rather than sew them up. It's a quick and neat method, and easy to pull out if you make a mistake. You can use this method on the wrong side or the right side, depending on the effect you require.

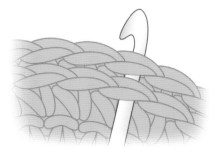

1 Put the edges to be joined side by side, matching the stitches. Insert the hook under both loops of a stitch in both pieces. Wrap the yarn round the hook and pull a loop through.

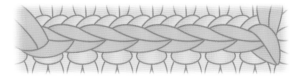

2 Work a row of double crochet, inserting the hook through the stitches of both pieces each time. It's the same process as working double crochet in the usual way; just treat both pieces as a single piece.

The same principle can be used to slip stitch pieces together, working through the back loop only (see page 117). If you are looking down on an edge from above, the back loop is the loop on the outside of the edge. Insert the hook through the back loops of both pieces and slip stitch them together (see page 118).

Tassels and fringes

It is quick and easy to add a fringe to a piece of crochet.

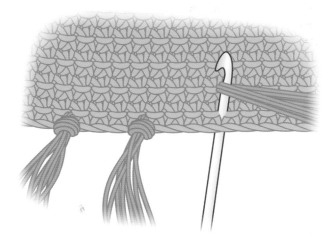

1 Cut the length of yarn as stated in the pattern. Fold a bundle of strands in half. With right side of the work facing, insert a crochet hook from the wrong side through one of the edge stitches. At the fold point, catch the bunch of strands with the hook.

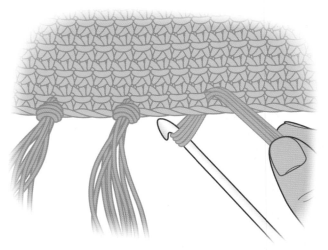

2 Pull the fold through the work to the back. Take out the hook to leave a loop.

3 Using your fingers, pull the tails of the bunch of strands through the loop.

4 Pull on the tails to tighten the loop firmly and secure the tassel.

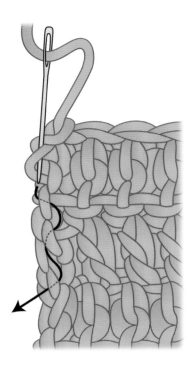

Weaving in yarn ends

It is important to weave in the tail ends of the yarn so that they are secure and your crochet won't unravel. Thread a tapestry needle with the tail end of yarn. On the wrong side, take the needle through the crochet one stitch down on the edge, then take it through the stitches, working in a gentle zigzag. Work through four or five stitches then return in the opposite direction. Remove the needle, pull the crochet gently to stretch it and trim the end.

If there are a lot of ends to weave in, I prefer to do them as I go, or the task takes ages once the crochet is complete.

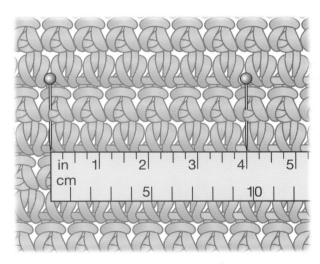

How to measure a tension square

Using the hook and the yarn recommended in the pattern, make a number of chains to measure approximately 15cm (6in). Working in the stitch pattern given for the tension measurements, work enough rows to form a square. Fasten off.

Take a ruler, place it horizontally across the square, and using pins, mark a 10cm (4in) area. Repeat vertically to form a 10cm (4in) square on the fabric.

Count the number of stitches across, and the number of rows within the square, and compare against the tension given in the pattern.

If your numbers match the pattern then use this size hook and yarn for your project. If you have more stitches, then your tension is tighter than recommended and you need to use a larger hook. If you have fewer stitches, then your tension is looser and you will need a smaller hook.

Make tension squares using different size hooks until you have matched the tension in the pattern, and use this hook to make the project.

Suppliers

Details of where to buy the yarns used in this book can be found through the following websites. If you can't find the exact yarns used, your local yarn store will be able to help you find a substitute.

Mrs Moon Plump and Fluff: www.mrsmoon.co.uk

Bernat: www.yarnspirations.com

Blue Sky Fibers: www.blueskyalpacas.com

Cascade: www.cascadeyarns.com

Lana Stop: www.lanasstop.com/en

Natali Stewart: www.natalistewart.co.uk

Nutscene Twine: www.nutscene.com

Rico: www.rico-design.de

Rooster: www.roosteryarns.com

Rowan: www.knitrowan.com

Sajou Metallic Thread: www.sajou.fr

Spud & Chloë: www.blueskyfibers.com

SweetGeorgia: www.sweetgeorgiayarns.com

Index

Acknowledgements

We've had great fun with *Simple Chic Crochet*, which has been made possible by the lovely people who support us every day.

Most importantly, ensuring that our second book has not suffered from 'tricky second album' syndrome has been our wonderful editor, Kate Haxell, who has been just as patient as ever, even considering the inclusion of charts that have given her that extra bit of work. Thank you Kate for still liking us (or pretending to anyway!); you have made it all so easy.

We must also thank the wonderfully talented Jenny Reid, who herself is an amazing crochet designer and Mrs Moon supporter and very very kindly worked up a few of the samples for us. We are very lucky to have such a kind and gifted friend!

Thank you to everyone at CICO Books, especially Cindy, Penny C (we hope we've tempted you to start crocheting), Sally, Vicky, Jo and Penny W for the beautiful design, styling and photography.

Finally, thank you to our lovely husbands, James and Tim, for all the hard work they put in to Mrs Moon behind the scenes – our new warehouse is a triumph, James! And our gorgeous children, Andrew, Florence, Ollie and Molly, Henry, Freddie (IT helpdesk!), Billy and Tilly… we'll get you making things yet!